THE SURGEON'S RHYME

RHYME

A Memoir

Dr Michael Barrie was born in London and educated at King's College School, Wimbledon, and St Thomas's Hospital Medical School. His first post as a doctor was at Kingston Hospital in 1991, and his second was as a junior psychiatrist at West Park Hospital, both in Surrey. He is married and now lives and practises as a GP in Kingston upon Thames. He has contributed over sixty articles to medical journals, including *The Lancet*. *The Surgeon's Rhyme* is Dr Barrie's first book.

THE SURGEON'S RHYME

A Memoir

Michael Barrie

The Book Guild Ltd
Sussex, England

First published in Great Britain in 2004 by
The Book Guild Ltd,
25 High Street,
Lewes, East Sussex
BN7 2LU

Typesetting in Bembo by
IML Typographers, Birkenhead, Merseyside

Printed in Great Britain by
Athenæum Press Ltd, Gateshead

A catalogue record for this book is
available from The British Library

ISBN 1 85776 813 2

For Robert and Alex

This book describes my life as a family doctor. I report events as they appeared to me; where necessary I have altered the names of professional colleagues and others. The case histories contained within these pages chronicle my encounters with patients: and here all names and identifying details have been changed.

Acknowledgements

This book would not have been possible had it not been for those individuals who contributed to my education and helped shape my early career.

To Peter Wicker, thank you for guiding me by your wisdom and leadership, and for your insistence that your pupils have forbearance in all that they do. Likewise I thank the late Richard Dawson who inspired me, quite literally, to appreciate the written and spoken language; I shall always be grateful.

My thanks to Stephen Foot who brought his academic subject alive by his superb teaching. It is because of him that I succeeded in chemistry and consequently enjoyed the related discipline of biochemistry. I maintain to this day an appreciation of the elegance of the multitude of organic reactions and pathways that comprise the human body's everyday function. The debt I owe Stephen goes further; by encouraging me to pursue printing as a hobby he fired in me an enthusiasm for typefaces, letterheads, book style and publishing. This book is a product of his inspiration.

There are those too, too many to name individually if indeed I could even recall each of them, who have encouraged me on the wards, in clinics, casualty, theatres and, latterly, general practice. To them, thank you.

To my partners at Richmond Road Medical Centre, thank you.

To Joanna Bentley, my editor at The Book Guild Publishers, thank you for your valuable assistance in shaping this book into its finished form.

An especially big thank you to Marc Sherwood. I am indebted to him for his astute suggestions, unflagging support whenever I wavered on abandoning the book, thoughtful criticism and enduring encouragement. He provided humour when the going got tough and was a sounding board to many a dilemma. It is Marc who deserves the ultimate credit for *The Surgeon's Rhyme* having been written.

And of course thank you to my wife, Roopal – for everything.

All too often time and circumstance lead us to the view that patients are tireless devourers of our energies, and that for all practical purposes we must go on giving until we die, or give up the unequal struggle with Nature and her diseases. This is to ignore the view that patients can be a source of nutrition: not just in the sense of providing us with our daily bread and butter, but also in the sense of nourishing our personalities. They do this by telling us about ourselves. You may think that you are kind and wise, or clumsy and inadequate, and it takes our patients to disabuse us of these illusions and to show us that some days we are good, and some days we are bad. Thanks to our patients, we never stay the same. After practising medicine for a decade or so, our minds become populated by the ghosts of former patients, beckoning us, warning us, reminding us of the things we cannot control – and the ideals to which we aspire. We are lucky to work in a profession in which experience counts for more than knowledge, and it is to augment this thirst for experience that we urge our readers to turn away from learning by rote: let us read novels, cultivate our friends, travel far and wide – and try to keep forever curious, for then, if we are lucky, we stand to gain that priceless therapeutic asset: a rich and compassionate personality, and we will be all the more inclined to reformulate this tiresome and inconvenient patient who now confronts us into a lovable series of imperfections, joined together by bits of glory.

J.A.B. Collier, J.M. Longmore and T.J. Hodgetts,
Oxford Handbook of Clinical Specialties,
Fourth Edition, Oxford University Press.

1

berry • n. (pl. **–ies**) **1** a small roundish juicy fruit without a stone.
▶ Botany: any fruit that has its seeds enclosed in a fleshy pulp, for
example a banana or tomato. **2** a fish egg or roe of a lobster or
similar creature.

— DERIVATIVES **berried** adj. **berrying** n.
— ORIGIN OE *berie*, of Gmc origin.

The Concise Oxford Dictionary
Tenth Edition, Oxford University Press.

Maggie Halsall must have wished she had never come to
see me. Her middle-aged face, contorted with worry and
angst, told of her disquiet.

'Oh doctor,' she said for the fourth time. 'What should
I do?'

Once more I spelt out her options. I had noted these
down onto a sheet of paper and underlined each as it was
discussed, with the result that the piece of paper presented
an untidy, though scientifically valid, algorithm of
sequential alternatives.

It had begun with a consultation a few weeks before.
Mrs Halsall had varicose veins which she thought were
unsightly. She had shown me the offending varicosities

and I had said that the only effective treatment was surgery.

'Strip them out,' I had said emphatically. 'The surgeon makes a nick in the groin, threads a length of wire like a bicycle's brake cable down the vein, and keeps pushing until it emerges down by the ankle where he's made another little cut in your vein.'

'How ghastly!' she said.

'Oh, there's worse to come,' I warned. 'He attaches a little metal bung securely onto the ankle-end of the wire, and then pulls for all he's worth.'

'Pulls?' exclaimed Mrs Halsall.

'Yes, pulls. Pulls so hard that he strips the vein right out of the leg.'

'Ouch! And then I'll be rid of the ghastly thing?'

'Yes. But he'll need to do both sides, of course.'

'Oooh ... he can do both at the same time? He's got enough wire?'

We had both laughed. I had said I would refer her to the hospital.

I dictate my referral letters at home. It allows time to check a patient's file for past history, details of previous operations and so on. Many years ago a chap presented himself at my surgery with deafness. No relevant past history, he said. Examination with my auriscope was entirely normal: his external auditory canals were healthy and wax-free, revealing unhindered views of both ear drums, which looked fine. Various drugs can produce hearing loss but No, he had assured me, he wasn't taking any medication. I decided to refer him to an ear, nose and throat specialist. Several outpatient appointments and two fearfully expensive scans later and the cause of his hearing loss was established: previous meningeal infection.

'Meningitis?' I exclaimed when next I saw him.

'Yeah, that's what they said.'

'You never told me you've had meningitis,' I said.

'You never asked,' he quipped.

Sure enough in his medical file there was a hospital discharge summary giving details of his recovery from bacterial meningitis. Another lesson, I thought, in the need to be meticulous.

And so whilst Robert and Alex, my two young sons, careered around the garden, I delved into Mrs Halsall's file in order to familiarise myself with her past medical history. The physicians' entries relating to her childhood illnesses were of little import but there were some letters in her file which told an altogether more startling story. In fact I was so taken aback that to this day I can recall guiltily the pleasurable tingle of my daunting discovery.

The story began – *begins*, even, as it is ongoing – when

Mrs Halsall was twenty-one years of age. A fading and very ragged carbon copy of a letter from her GP asks the duty casualty officer to see her. The lass has, the letter explains, a severe headache which came on abruptly. She is fretful and anxious and 'undoubtedly has acute nervous exhaustion'.

The casualty officer dismisses the GP's suggestion and reckons she has had a brain haemorrhage. Nowadays such a hunch can quickly be proven (or disproven) by a brain scan, but it wasn't that simple in 1971. Then the diagnosis of a bleed into the brain was made by elucidating subtle clinical symptoms and signs, and by the presence of blood within the cerebrospinal fluid that surrounds the brain. This can be 'tapped off' by lumbar puncture and the foresighted casualty doctor did just that. He inserted a needle into the base of Maggie Halsall's spine and fluid spurted out. Not only was it under considerable pressure, it was the colour of tomato ketchup.

Our brains are protected by three thin layers. The middle of these is the arachnoid layer, from the Greek *arachne* (for spider) and so-called because it bridges over the grooves on the surface of the brain. Within these grooves are chunky blood vessels and, with the arachnoid draped over them, one can perhaps appreciate the connection with our eight-legged friends.

The large vessels nestling in the clefts of the brain can rupture, with the result that there is sudden filling of the space under the arachnoid membrane. This is known as a subarachnoid haemorrhage and is the main cause of spontaneous stroke in young people. Needless to say, it is a very dangerous condition and the death rate is high.

The commonest cause of a subarachnoid haemorrhage is rupture of a pre-existing arterial swelling (or, properly, 'aneurysm' from the Greek *anaeurusma*, a widening). An aneurysm usually occurs at branching points on an artery and is due to a congenital weakness of the arterial wall which, over time, gives rise to a small, berry-like swelling. It represents the ultimate hidden danger – a time-bomb where an individual is unaware of its presence until it suddenly ruptures.

The onset of a subarachnoid haemorrhage is marked by severe and sudden headache. Sufferers characteristically spin around to see who has hit them on the back of the head. Pain is followed by loss of consciousness and, if the bleeding does not stop, by death.

There is a morbid 'rule of thirds': one-third of patients with subarachnoid haemorrhage drop dead; another third die within a week; one-third have a further bleed, usually within a fortnight; and one-third survive. Of this third, only one-third are symptom-free after a year. Only one third of the third that bleed again, survive.

Treatment is directed at keeping the blood pressure reasonably low, preventing blood vessels going into spasm (the body's well-intentioned defence mechanism to stem the bleeding, which paradoxically causes the neurological damage of a stroke), and surgery. The operation involves 'clipping' the neck of the aneurysm but it carries a considerable morbidity and mortality.

There's not much anyone can do about any of this. Unless, that is, you happen to know that you are walking around with a berry aneurysm inside your head. And this, as I'll explain in a while, is exactly what Mrs Halsall found out in my consulting room that afternoon.

The letters in her file tell an amazing story. The casualty officer, as I've already said, thought she had a sub-arachnoid haemorrhage; the increased pressure of her cerebrospinal fluid, and the blood within it, confirmed the diagnosis. He referred her urgently to the neurosurgical team. But remember, no fancy scans in those days. The neurosurgeon, an eminent chap, I am told, examined Maggie and agreed that Yes, it was indeed a subarachnoid haemorrhage. The neurosurgeon was at that time performing a research study whereby he randomly allocated patients with brain haemorrhages into one of two treatment groups. One group was managed in the usual fashion – an operation to locate the berry aneurysm and then apply a clip; clotted blood can be removed from the subarachnoid space and the clip prevents a re-bleed. The aneurysm is left *in vivo* but will cause no further bother: the little clip sees to that.

Spare a thought, then, for the other group. Incredibly, the poor souls were left alone. *Left alone!* No active treatment, other than basic nursing care. Outrageous!

I have since spoken to the neurosurgeon's successor, who grimly informed me that the trial was halted prematurely on account of the high death rate. Nowadays there are 'ethics committees' that scrutinise proposals for trials and studies, banning those that compromise a patient's care.

So Maggie Halsall is seen by the consultant neurosurgeon. A coin is flipped and, hey presto, she is assigned to the *non-intervention* arm of his study. She is taken to a ward where later that day she slips into a coma. She would die of dehydration – if the haemorrhage doesn't kill her first – and so the duty doctor inserts a cannula into the back of her hand and administers fluids intravenously. Young Maggie stays in a coma for almost three weeks, being kept alive as much by the saline and glucose being dripped into her body as by the visits of her doting family who maintain their presence by her bedside.

By the rule of thirds she should have died. By a miracle she survived.

I pushed the pile of hospital letters aside and took a deep breath. The last one was from the eminent specialist to the GP. 'I am thankful to have been involved in this girl's care,' it concludes, 'and pleased that she has made a complete recovery without my having to resort to perilous surgery where the outcome may not have been so favourable.'

What should I do? I could see that one problem would beget another. Mrs Halsall must have an aneurysm inside her head. After all, she survived only because the bleeding, mercifully, stopped of its own accord. As the blood under the arachnoid was reabsorbed by her body, she slowly regained consciousness. But the berry aneurysm must still be there.

Assuming it is (and I could think of no reason why it shouldn't), then oughtn't it be clipped? Or do we say that it has been there for the best part of thirty years without re-bleeding, so best leave it be?

Should I even tell her? Why not just write to the

vascular surgeons asking them to strip out her varicose veins? After all, my predecessor referred her to the maternity unit when she was pregnant without even mentioning her previous subarachnoid haemorrhage, let alone the fact that it hadn't been clipped. Maybe he made the same discovery in her medical file but considered it best to say nowt. She subsequently gave birth to a baby girl: the surge in blood pressure during the second stage of her labour didn't cause the berry aneurysm to pop.

No, I thought. I cannot conceal what I have learnt. How terrible it would be if she were to have a further bleed in, say, a few years' time? How would I admit to the family that I knew she was harbouring an aneurysm? Or would I just claim ignorance? After all, there's no legal obligation to read the past correspondence of your patients' files. New patients join my list every day – I cannot possibly plough through the reams of letters stuffed inside their medical records.

No, I must tell her and suggest she has it clipped. Hang on! Tell her about my discovery, yes. But *suggest* it be clipped? What if she has it clipped and the operation kills her or causes a stroke?

Worries, worries, worries. I wrote her a short note asking her to come and see me in the surgery.

'You don't think my varicose veins are bad enough to cut out?' she ventured a couple of weeks later.

'No,' I smiled ruefully and explained the saga of the letters in her file.

'I never knew,' she said finally. 'I always thought that I'd had a mystery brain condition and, yes, I could've died but was lucky to pull through. My family prayed night and day for me, you know.'

'I'm sorry,' I said quietly.

She ignored my apology. 'But my parents never said anything about a haemorrhage,' she continued, 'or maybe they weren't told either. I just don't know.'

I drew a picture of the arteries that traverse the base of the brain and then added a berry aneurysm to the sketch.

'So this could rupture again?' asked Mrs Halsall.

'The risk of that happening is between one and two per cent every year,' I replied.

I could see her eyes fix on the ceiling in concentration whilst she did the arithmetic.

'I'm fifty-two, so ... er ... if I live to eighty that's...'

'Sixty per cent,' I said, adding, 'at the worst.'

'Blimey. But maybe I'd survive next time.' She shuddered. 'I did last time,' she said wanly.

I didn't want to go into the rule of thirds: that would

be unfair and would burden her with too much statistical information.

'But having the berry aneurysm clipped isn't without risk either,' I replied gloomily. I went on to say that fifteen per cent of patients who have their aneurysms clipped either die on the operating table or have a stroke. 'At best,' I continued, 'you wake up the same person you are now; at worst you have a stroke or die.'

'But if the operation goes well then I *won't* be the same person. You're wrong there, surely? I'll be safe from that berry thingummy from bursting.'

'Yes,' I conceded. 'But then who's to say it will burst? You've got through half your life without a problem. And if it ruptures you might die on the spot. If on the other hand you go for the op and, say, have a stroke, well...' I petered out.

'So what do I then, Dr Barrie?' Mrs Halsall's question, uttered in a hushed urgency, was pleading. A supplication, even.

'I think the first thing is to see what the angiogram's doing.'

'What do you mean?' she asked.

'Well, whether it's large or small, where it is in the brain, you know – that kind of thing. It might even be in too risky a place to contemplate surgery.'

'And how do we find all this out?'

'I can arrange for you to have a cerebral angiogram.'

'But there's no point having this if I don't want surgery, right?'

'Wrong,' I said rather too harshly. 'Berry aneurysms can run in families.'

'Oh God!' said Mrs Halsall. 'You never mentioned that.'

'Yes, but...'

'But we know I must have a berry-thing because I had the haemorrhage, didn't I?'

'There are other, rarer causes of subarachnoid haemorrhage.' I explained.

'Then I'd better have an angiogram,' she said submissively.

The cerebral angiogram showed a large berry aneurysm on her left middle cerebral artery. I arranged for her to see a neurosurgeon and they spent an hour or so weighing up the pros and cons of an operation. After much soul-searching, Mrs Halsall decided against surgery. Had she been younger, she argued, it might have been different. But she wasn't, and that was that.

Her daughter is my patient and I sought permission from

Mrs Halsall to broach the subject with her, suggesting that they attend my surgery together. Last week we discussed the same issues that were only too familiar to her mother. I explained that berry aneurysms can have a genetic basis, that is that in some cases they are inherited. I told them the annual risk of rupture.

The atmosphere was tense, more so because of the girl's young age: she is twenty-one, the age her mother was when she'd had her bleed. And she is expecting her first child.

More worries.

'What was that about the blood pressure going up in labour, doctor?'

2

August 1st 1991. Long before the day I was due to start
work as a doctor, I realised that it would be in my best
interests to feign superior knowledge, clinical wisdom and
confidence. Above all, confidence. And so it came to pass
that on a bright August morning I climbed the stairs to the
sixth floor of the main clinical block at Kingston Hospital.
The hospital has its origins in a Victorian workhouse and
its buildings comprise an untidy assortment of very old,
not-so-old and 1970s blocks, juxtaposed amongst three
state-of-the-art creations.

My predecessor, Dr Melanie Hiorns, unclipped the
'bleep' from the waistband of her skirt, handed me a scrap
of paper on which she had scribbled the names of twenty-
seven patients, and wished me the best of luck.

'You'll need this,' said Hiorns. 'Each and every one of
these is yours. Might be a good idea to do a quick ward
round now and introduce yourself. You'll need to know
everything about them. What's wrong with them, their
drugs, their numbers, their –'

'I'm sorry?' I interrupted. '*Numbers*?

'Yes,' she said. 'Numbers are blood results. You know – sodium values, potassium and so on. Usual rubbish.' She flicked her hair back. Blimey, I thought, she really is confident. What the hell happens when she's gone? 'So here's your list,' she continued. 'The Mess is on the ground floor. The code for the door is 123. Oh, and here's my bleep.' She smiled and was gone.

Bloody hell. I turned to the nurses' station. Three nurses, seated around the main desk, suddenly looked down and wrote furiously in the case notes before them. I ambled over toward them. I knew that I looked fresh-faced and eager although this belied the feeling of fear within.

'Hi! I'm Michael Barrie,' I said brashly. 'Call me Mike. It's all a bit new for me here.' They seemed friendly but were weary of the six-monthly change in junior medical staff. Another doctor: uncertainty, yet again, over whether he was going to be likeable. And then it started all over again. Melanie Hiorns was popular, that much I could sense; moreover, she was organised. Efficient.

Over the days that followed I gradually got the hang of things. I organised systems for blood tests, electro-cardiograms and X-ray requests. I did my 'rounds' on patients. I stayed awake, bleary-eyed, during my nights on call. And I fell in love. But I mustn't bore you, dear reader, at least not just yet.

15

What bothered me most was the irrelevance of just about everything I had learnt at medical school. Five years of pretty intense education, but for what purpose? I studied anatomy, physiology, pharmacology, biochemistry, microbiology, histopathology, but now it seemed I might as well have done a degree in ancient history. Sure, there were ill patients on the ward and a bit of medical knowledge didn't go amiss, but most of the time I was a clerk. I seemed to be forever ordering investigations – urine tests, blood tests, sputum cultures, X-rays or whatever. I realise now that the first year of medical practice doesn't involve an awful lot of medicine, but at the time I was gobsmacked. I was frightened and scared that I wouldn't be able to cope with the horrors of acute clinical medicine and yet in the end I was nothing better than a secretary with 'Dr' in front of my name.

I spent a year at Kingston Hospital, first as a medical house officer for six months then as a surgical house officer for the remaining six months. In the medical post, I worked for a chest physician but that didn't mean a damn thing; Kingston is a general hospital and all manner of illnesses present at its accident and emergency department. If they were adult and didn't need cutting open then they were pushed in the direction of the on-call medical team. If, for instance, a chap with a heart attack came to A&E –

whether brought by ambulance or having been referred by his GP – it was immaterial whether the gastroenterological team were 'on call' that night, or the chest team, or any other team you care to mention. Surely, you might be thinking, it would be lucky for the patient if he happens to have his heart attack when the cardiological team are on call. Or the asthmatic who by good fortune is admitted on a Tuesday when *my* team, the noble and fine chest team, are on? No, not at all. The so-called cardiologist, having qualified only a few weeks back, is no more a heart specialist than I, fresh from St Thomas's Hospital Medical School, am a chest physician.

Each junior doctor, whatever his supposed specialty, would admit a rag-bag bunch of patients with problems such as angina, heart attacks, strokes and breathing difficulties. My yield would be no different. My consultant might or might not see them on his ward round but it was my job to look after them for the rest of the week. And I did not complain!

I was determined not to allow the high administrative duties of the job to detract from what I considered to be its main objective: to gain a grounding in clinical practice. There were vast amounts of forms to complete and tasks that required only the basics of commonsense but I resolved to gain a lot more besides.

There was a fascinating study published in *The Journal of the Royal Society of Medicine* a little while ago by Peter Goodfellow, a consultant surgeon in Sheffield. He looked at eight clinical skills required of junior doctors: the taking of blood from a vein in the arm, performing an arterial blood gas estimation, rectal examination and so on. He found that a substantial number had little or no experience in these core skills; for example, almost one-third had never catheterised a patient. Medical students receive the bulk of their teaching from consultant-grade doctors and are more often than not ignored by the junior doctors who perform these 'hands-on' duties. ECGs, venesection and blood gases are the province of newly-qualified doctors but they are simply too busy to teach these procedures to students. So new juniors experience a baptism of fire when they first don their doctors' coats, and the cycle continues unbroken.

Indeed, after six months at Kingston Hospital I had learnt how to deal with a wide range of conditions and medical emergencies, and it has been of immeasurable help for the years in practice that followed.

Before long I had struck up a relationship with a beautiful staff nurse on the ward. Her name was Roopal and she was the most attractive girl I'd ever met. How appropriate, then, that her name is the Hindi word for 'beautiful'. I loved her sensitive yet warm personality; I loved her funny sense of humour; I loved being with her: in fact I had fallen in love with her.

Any free time I had I spent with Roopal and was naturally over the moon that I had chosen to work my second six months at the same hospital. Great! I had naïvely assumed that evenings not spent on call would be my own to enjoy as I wished. I couldn't have been more wrong! The surgical job was a nightmare from beginning to end: the day began at 7 o'clock in the morning with a ward round, followed by a manic rush to order the daily blood tests and X-rays, write up the clinical notes on the patients awaiting routine surgery, scribble a theatre list (so that the operating theatre nurses would know in which order to summon patients from the ward), and then check the medication charts on the ward patients. On top of all of this I had to obtain the signed consent of the patients due to be operated on that day – and be available to assist in theatre if the going got rough. Throughout this my bleep constantly bleep-bleeped.

'Oh, is that Dr Barrie? This is Astor ward. Your chap with the appendix is spiking a temperature. Can you come?'

'Michael? Good. It's Jackie on Albany ward. The gall bladder lady is back from theatre but I think her blood pressure is dropping. You'll be here soon, won't you?'

'Dr Barrie? Sorry to nag but you must get that girl to sign the consent form for her varicose veins. Theatres are refusing to send for her until it's been done.'

And so on, and on. I would start one job, only to be pulled away to another. I felt as if I was forever chasing my tail until the day eventually ground to a halt with a second, and final, ward round at 7 o'clock. The 'round' would finish at a quarter to eight. It meant I was working a thirteen-hour day. On every third day and every third weekend, I stayed at the hospital after the evening ward round and worked through the night. It was exhausting and I just couldn't see myself surviving the duration of the job.

The Government had recently launched their 'New Deal' on junior doctors' hours. The Minister of Health, Virginia Bottomley, working closely with the British Medical Association, had urged health authorities to cooperate in an aggressive drive to cut the long hours doctors worked. Her successor, Brian Mawhinney, wrote to all doctors in June 1992 stating:

Our underlying aim is to bring hours worked down to no more than an average of 56 a week. I am convinced that by continuing to work together we shall succeed in bringing an end to the long-standing

20

problem of the excessive hours worked by junior doctors.

Good on yer, I thought at the time. Yeah, good old Brian!

Within a few days, one of the surgical consultants at Kingston summoned all the house officers into his poky office. The room faced the courtyard; over his shoulder I could see nurses in the ward opposite trying to manoeuvre a patient onto a commode. There were six of us present in the top dog's office and the atmosphere was stifling.

'Right,' he said abruptly in the way that most surgeons speak. 'As you know, I have been told, no *instructed*, by the local health authority to reduce your long hours.' He paused after he had said 'long' and then, contemptuously, rolled his eyes upwards. 'So,' he continued, 'if anyone should ask what hours you work, just stare them in the eye and say "nine to five" OK?'

'I'm sorry?' I asked sheepishly. 'I don't understand.'

'Oh for God's sake! There's always one, isn't there?' The surgeon looked at my fellow house officers but their faces displayed the same baffled expression as my own. 'I'll have to spell it out then. I expect all of you to start the day at 7 a.m. and leave after the evening ward round at a quarter to eight. But the official line is that you start at 9 a.m. and finish at 5 p.m. Clear?' He glowered pointedly at me before picking up a slim sheaf of papers from his desk and handed them round to the assembled junior doctors.

I could see it was a newsletter, which I guessed he'd written himself, and it expounded the virtues of the New Deal. It read:

> The change in junior doctor's [sic] hours mean new working arrangements will be implemented. The normal working day is 9 a.m to 5 p.m. I am sure that revisions will become necessary as we progress and I look forward to your comments.

'So you've *written* that we should work from nine to five but are *saying* something else. Does that mean you are …' I trailed off, knowing that I was causing trouble for myself.

'I am doing what, Dr Barrie?'

It would be pointless trying to argue the point here. But so incensed was I by the man's dishonesty that later that day I wrote to him saying: 'All house officers are expected to be on the ward by 7 a.m. and leave at 8.30 p.m. I thought you should be aware of this state of affairs.'

In his terse reply he wrote:

> Thank you for your letter. I thought my earlier communication [the newsletter handed out earlier]

was clear enough. The working day is 9 a.m. to 5 p.m. It is these hours that I expect to be worked. You must not work any additional hours. I would be grateful if you could let me know who this is causing concern to, as I will then speak to them and endeavour to sort out any misconceptions they may have.

You, I thought, you're the tosser.

What to do now? I wrote to the chief executive of the hospital, explaining the problem and asking for his help. He replied:

The consultant surgeons are adamant that they have issued the appropriate instructions. Your contracted hours are 9 a.m. to 5 p.m. and you must adhere to them. I have to say that my prime aim is to reduce the hours of junior doctors. It would be inappropriate for me to encourage doctors to work additional hours.

Bloody hell. Now I was stuck: the mighty powers within the hospital knew perfectly well that the junior surgical doctors were working an excessive number of hours, decreed by the Government as illegal, but were refusing to recognise this. There was only one option left to me: to act as whistleblower. I thought long and hard about this. The obvious benefit of lopping five hours off every working day was hugely attractive but I wasn't so goddamned stupid that I didn't realise that my career in medicine would be curtailed less than twelve months after qualifying. I remember very clearly the torment this caused me.

One evening a patient was admitted with pancreatitis. Billy Gibbon was young, no more than thirty perhaps, and in severe pain. I set up an intravenous infusion and pumped in saline and pain killers. I was called back to Billy's bedside six or seven times that night. The accident and emergency department was heaving with patients on trolleys waiting for me to examine them. It was slow work; no sooner had I begun to see one than my bleep would sound, signalling that I had to return to the ward in order to increase Billy Gibbon's morphine dosage.

All the while I had one thing on my mind: do I telephone the British Medical Association and tip them off? Tell them that I am working in excess of one hundred hours every week? The consequences would be dire, for sure. The consultant surgeon – the asshole with the poky office and shitty newsletter – would refuse to sign the requisite form which would allow me to become a fully registered doctor (newly-qualified doctors are provisionally registered with the General Medical Council until 'successful' completion of two house officer posts). I suspected that if I were to grass up the consultant-in-charge for making the juniors work illegal hours then he would refuse to sign the form on the grounds that my performance had not been 'successful'.

For a few days I considered the issue carefully. I reckoned that I had just too much to lose. However, it wasn't until a further week had passed that the issue was at last laid to rest in my mind. I think it was a Monday, because that was the day of the consultant ward round. We had reached the bed of Billy Gibbon; his pancreatitis had settled and, no longer in pain, he hoped that he might be discharged. The entourage formed itself into a gaggle of white-coated bodies at the end of his bed. Seven pairs of eyes were fixed on Billy as he was asked whether his pain had indeed abated.

'Oh yes, doctors,' he said. 'I haven't even got so much as an ache now.'

'Good, good,' one of the registrars said. There was a medical student present and the registrar turned to address her. 'What should we advise Mr Gibbon here to do when he gets home?'

The student was baffled.

'I don't know,' she said finally.

'Well,' said the registrar, 'tell me the causes of pancreatitis.'

The poor girl remained baffled. She was studying medicine at Southampton and had come to Kingston for a fortnight of provincial experience away from her *alma mater*. There was an uncomfortable silence whilst she thought of something to say to the group of doctors who faced her expectantly. Over the top of her head I saw a young man in a sports jacket and light chinos enter the ward by the door at the far end. He spoke briefly with the ward clerk, who nodded and then pointed at us, and I watched as the man approached our group. The medical student hadn't answered and, mistaking the silence for an invitation to speak, the stranger introduced himself.

'Good morning doctors,' he said; then, nodding to the nurse conducting the ward round, 'Sister. I'm Dr John Knight-Smith from the BMA. I'm on the Task Force set up to check that individual hospitals are, you know, entering into the spirit of the New Deal. This is going through Parliament soon and so we're very keen to see that hospitals have taken the necessary steps to ensure that they shall be complying with the law. Oh, I'm sorry,' he said, glancing around, 'I should've asked. Who's the consultant?'

He must know the answer, I thought, as he had directed

his question to the consultant. It had struck me as odd when I started at Kingston Hospital that the consultant staff were conspicuous by the absence of their white coat. Every doctor in the hospital wore one except for the consultants, they wore 'business' suits. I never understood the reason for this.

The consultant stepped forward and shook hands with the guy from the Task Force.

'We intend to visit every hospital within the next six months,' Knight-Smith continued. He seemed a nice guy: a genuine sort of chap. 'When I did the first lot of visits I spoke only to the consultant but I got an uneasy feeling that a lot of the time I wasn't being told the whole story. You know, the truth.' He looked around the group in front of him. 'But now I make a point of speaking to the consultant in front of his team. It's got to be transparent. I want the house officer to have his say. Even the patients should butt in if they want. After all, they're the ones who see how hard the juniors really work. They'll have an idea of what hours are being worked. We've got to make sure that working long hours becomes a thing of the past. Tired doctors are lousy doctors. Worse, they're dangerous and no patient needs that!' He smiled encouragingly at Billy Gibbon. I liked Knight-Smith. He really was going to help, I could tell. I admired him for interrupting his medical career to tackle the plight of doctors and so improve their working conditions.

'We're delighted to welcome you to our ward round,' said the surgical consultant. 'At Kingston we take the issue of reducing our juniors' hours very, very seriously. All our house officers work from nine in the morning until five in the afternoon. The on-call hours are additional, of course, but I'm proud to say that we've accomplished the recommendation of the New Deal with ease. I think it fair to say that no doctor works more than fifty-six hours per week. I've given every doctor my written assurance that these are the contracted hours they work. So it would appear, Dr Knight-Smith,' he said, turning to the visitor, 'that there isn't a problem here, is there?' The consultant fixed his gaze on me for several seconds and then focussed his attention on the student. 'The registrar was hoping you might enlighten us on the causes of pancreatitis?'

'The only one I can remember is gall stones,' replied the student.

'Look, I'd better be off,' Dr Knight-Smith interrupted. 'I have to visit another hospital this afternoon and I want to complete my report on this one first. I'm delighted that the conditions here are OK. It's so nice to meet a consultant that takes such a keen interest in looking after his juniors. Anyway, if you'll excuse me?' He shook hands with the consultant and gave a small, apologetic grin to the patient.

'Just a little hint,' he said quietly to the medical student as he made to leave. 'Best think of disease causation under distinct headings. I know a little rhyme that might help. Let me see ... um ... yes, I've got it: Heredity, sex and age, Occupation, race and clime, The ills that men are subject to, The vices of our time.'

He beamed at his own ability to remember the verse, then straightening his tie he nodded to Sister and strode off.

My head was swimming. How sweetly familiar those lines were to me. For just a few delicious seconds I sensed the warmth similar to that experienced on hearing a long-forgotten tune with a special significance. I knew the harmonious lines he had recounted but now all I could feel was betrayal.

I was sickened by the utter despair of the whole thing. I was vaguely aware of the registrar telling the student about the perils of alcoholism and how Billy Gibbon must swear that he will never again touch a drop of the stuff if he wants to avoid a life of endless admissions with chronic alcohol-induced pancreatitis.

I felt helpless and hopeless. I didn't know anything any more.

Except for one thing, that is: I knew where Knight-Smith had gone to medical school.

3

Medical school was, in all truth, a whole new ball game. I had applied to various learned establishments, choosing, ultimately, St Thomas's Hospital Medical School as its canteen had delicious, stuffed pitta-bread sandwiches and tea was served in chunky white mugs. I fancied the idea of studying in the heart of the capital and St Thomas's has an enviable position across the water from the Mother of Parliaments.

The first day was spent cutting up a poor tramp who had unwittingly left his body 'for the good of science and the furtherance of medical education'. Dissection is too elegant a word for it implies neatness and a careful hand on the part of the dissector. If only the tramp knew...

Lectures followed lectures which followed yet more lectures. It seemed more normal to have a headache than not, and just to make your head more sore, tutorials were squeezed into any remaining gap.

Students form themselves into little cliques, which always amazes me. How do, for instance, the Hooray Henrys know where to find their fellow brethren in a huge establishment such as St Thomas's? Likewise the Sloane. And the intellectual half-wits. What about the rugger buggers? How can they tell that a well-built student isn't just fat? I saw myself as boringly normal, eligible for membership of the 'standard' clique.

It must have been about six months into the course when I was made aware that 'they' intended to whittle us down.

'We call it pruning,' the Dean had said to the near-one-hundred-strong year group. I found his use of the royal first person singular cowardly: was he too chicken to admit that he had taken in too many of us in the first place? Pruning – my arse!

'Each medical school,' he continued, 'has a quota of doctors that it must see graduate, er, five years from now. Here at St Thomas's we want the best. The most able. So...' his eyes darted amongst and around the sea of young hopefuls in front of him, 'we weed out four or five students in the first year, and a slightly smaller number in the second year. Fail one exam, you take it again. Fail it a second time, you're out, sonny.'

The girls turned the corners of their mouths down at his deliberate use of masculine chummy-talk. I later realised that this was a St Thomas's tradition. And like all traditions was something which the alumni of the college seemed

31

reluctant to change. Pah! Well, we did lose students. I forget how many but I know they were jolly decent folk and probably would have made far finer doctors than many of those who qualified with me in 1991.

St Thomas's Hospital. What a place! An institution so steeped in history and tradition that you almost – *almost* – consider it irreverent for it to have embraced modern technology.

The hospital is named after St Thomas the Apostle, variously known as Doubting Thomas or Thomas Didymus (*didymus* is Aramaic for 'twin', so he was Thomas the Twin). This was not always so, however, because when the name 'St Thomas' was first applied to the little infirmary of the priory of St Mary Overy in 1173, it was St Thomas à Becket who was the patron saint. Thomas à Becket was martyred in 1170, having been notoriously murdered by the knights of King Henry II at Canterbury, and canonised in 1173.

The Act of Supremacy in 1534, which declared King Henry VIII to be Supreme Head of the Church of England, was followed by the Reformation, that religious upheaval which turned Roman Catholic England into a constitutionally Protestant country. The Reformation was accompanied by the Dissolution of the Monasteries: St Thomas's, a religious institution, was doomed. In 1540

Thomas Cromwell, the man employed to carry through the King's revolution, closed the hospital.

It was re-opened eleven years later by the 'boy-king', Edward VI, who insisted, however, that the hospital cease to function as a religious foundation. Instead, it was to be run by a board of governors, reporting to him. Immediately, it had a problem in finding a new name for the hospital. It had been closed for such a short time that it never lost its old name, and the empty building was still very much known as St Thomas's Hospital. The monarchy hated Thomas à Becket and had ordered that all statues of him be destroyed; yet it was vital to find a new name for the hospital, and the masterly idea was concocted to change its patronage to Thomas the Apostle.

And there you have it. St Thomas's Hospital lived on! Not so the medical school – but more of that later.

I spent the first two years concentrating on the theory of medicine, the study of the function *and functioning* of our wonderful bodies. Armed with oodles of meaningless knowledge, we then hit the wards to see disease, illness and suffering. I didn't realise until much later that this would be an unremitting chapter in my life. I would continue to meet – on a daily basis – sickness and human suffering; how naïve I must have been in those days.

Three clinical years were then spent in little chunks, called 'firms'. Each comprised seven medical students and in my firm I spent eight weeks attached to each specialty. I spent eight weeks on labour ward and in the obstetric clinics, eight weeks on the children's wards and eight weeks listening to inaudible heart murmurs.

'Oh, now I can hear it!' I would say, my ears strained to the stethoscope. But above the hum of the daily activity of the hospital I couldn't hear the heartbeat at all, let alone a super-added murmur caused by turbulent flow through a dodgy valve. Baffling! Years later, in the calm and hush of my own practice, all became clear and I started hearing things which I didn't know even existed!

And so it went on: rheumatology, orthopaedics, gastroenterology, psychiatry and more. But the most memorable has to have been general surgery, for it was here that I was introduced (although I am certain this is not the word he would have used to describe our encounter) to the most redoubtable doctor I have ever known.

Mr Eric Finch was St Thomas's senior surgeon. Late fifties, rounded shoulders, balding. And terrifyingly formidable. He was temperamental, abrupt and easily irritated. No one dared to cross his path, at least not intentionally, for his wont was to intimidate, deride and rebuke. But despite this – or maybe it was because of it – he was an excellent teacher; possibly the best. His measured words could be tetchy but they were the gems that moulded the doctors of tomorrow.

'Let's see,' he said on one occasion, looking across the patient's bed to Becky Stratton. Becky, a medical student on the firm, blushed as she realised that an interrogation had begun. As he spoke, Finch looked at the seven students assembled crescentically around the foot of the bed. 'Ah yes, Dr Stratton' he continued. 'This man has spent his life *smo*-king.' He paused before repeating, 'Smoking.' Finch abhorred cigarettes: those who smoked them and those who condoned them. Smoking – or *smo*-king as he liked to pronounce it, pulling his face into one of disgust – is, he said, the cause of unmentionable suffering. Far more than just disease and cancer. Oh no! *Smo*-king, he would say, is responsible for the fall of man from grace, the destruction of decent society as we know it. The final solution and worse. Legend has it that some smart-arse medical student once retorted, 'It's the source of your salary, sir, because if nobody smoked, then surely there would be no need for doctors like you, would there, sir?' That poor student, we are told, did not qualify as a doctor and had to eke out an existence somewhere far removed from the South Bank.

Becky waited for the great man to speak.

'Whereas I choose to go fishing at the weekend and you, Dr Stratton, no doubt gawp at the television, this patient *smo*-kes. But more than that, he smokes in his *work* time as well. His free time *and* his work time. Pathetic, I know, but there you have it.' Finch shot a glance at Becky Stratton, then at the patient, then at each of us in turn.

The patient, a thin chap in his fifties, seemed at first happy to be chosen as teaching 'matter', but now looked uncomfortable. I felt embarrassed for him. It was as if I represented the medical fraternity, the doctors' clan: the Finch Firm. Which of course I did. I glanced around and could see that my fellow students felt the same way. We were party to this patient's humiliation at the hands of his healer.

'And where did all this mindless *smo*-king get him, Dr Stratton? Where, I ask you, indeed?' He was in full flight, not pausing long enough for Becky to respond to his rhetorical questions. 'Bronchial carcinoma. Or *lung cancer* to all you half-wits. He has lung cancer. What, dear Dr Stratton, is the aetiology of lung cancer?'

Becky looked across at Mr Finch and smiled.

'Smok— I mean nicotine inhalation.' She was smiling

36

because the answer was obvious, or at least so she thought.

'NO!' he screamed. 'No! How many blasted times do I have to tell you the damned rhyme? Always use the rhyme.' Becky had fallen for the oldest trick in Eric Finch's book. As every student who had been on his firm knew, the aetiology – or *causation* – of any disease had to be considered according to his structured method. Or 'Eric's ditty' as it had been dubbed:

> *Heredity, sex and age,*
> *Occupation, race and clime,*
> *The ills that men are subject to –*
> *The vices of our time.*

It didn't matter if you were being grilled on the causation of pneumonia, the common cold or how a patient got a hairbrush stuck up his backside: you used the rhyme. Always. Never forget it, Finch would ruse, and it'll get you out of many a dilemma.

'Start again, Miss Stratton.' When he was angry, which was more often than he was cheerful, he would prefix his victim's name with a Miss or Mr. The ward round would start with Dr This and Dr That and Dr The Other. Then he would bemoan our ignorance. The veins on his scalp would stand proud and he would say: Poor Mr Barrie. He hasn't a clue, has he? Dr Levy, you tell him. Adam Levy, a dentist who had returned to university to study medicine, would attempt a guess. No! Finch would shout again. You're useless, Mr Levy, he would reprove – dropping the courtesy title – although Adam Levy is in fact very intelligent and now a well-respected consultant maxillofacial surgeon. Dr Hobbs, Finch would say, *you* enlighten us . . .

Back then to Becky, who now silently rehearsed the rhyme. 'Well, some types of lung cancer, Mr Finch, have a genetic basis. So I would wish to ask the patient if there's a family history of a similar problem.'

'Well, go on then. What are you waiting for?'

She turned to the pale, creased figure lying on the bed beneath her shoulders.

'Has anyone in your close family ever had any problems with coughing or breathlessness?' she ventured politely. She had a lovely bedside manner – kind and genuine. Becky is now a proficient consultant physician.

The patient shook his head in response and Becky turned to face Finch. 'Sex . . . I mean gender,' she said. 'I *think* it's more common in men. Yes, lung cancer is three times commoner in men than in women. It's also more likely with advancing age,' Becky paused, looking at Finch for encouragement. Unusually for him, a small smile had spread across his lips. He liked things done his way, and here was a student presenting an answer in the way he had taught.

'Occupation is a very important factor here,' said Becky.

'Determinant,' interrupted Finch.

'I'm sorry?'

'Determinant. Occupation is an important determinant.'

'Right.' Becky didn't quite see the advantage in his pedantic correction and she continued: 'Occupation is an important *determinant*. Working with asbestos gives a higher risk of lung cancer.' She inclined her head to the patient. He was weary of the extended bedside teaching session.

'No,' he said, anticipating the question. 'I was a minicab driver.'

'Thank you,' said Becky, repeating to Finch, 'He was a minicab driver.'

'I'm not deaf, Miss Stratton,' said Finch. 'But what about chromium, arsenic, you know – radioactive materials? They too can cause bronchial carcinoma. Anyway, go on Dr Stratton.'

Becky grinned at the sudden promotion. 'There's no difference in racial origin in this illness, and I don't think that the climate has anything to do with it either. Previous illness is important, Mr Finch. For example, bowel cancer can spread to the lungs. And other conditions can predispose to lung cancer. And, um, I think that's it, Mr Finch.' She glanced nervously at the rest of us. We all looked down, knowing that he would soon turn on somebody else.

'What do you mean that's it? What, you've finished?' His eyes had grown dark and small.

'There is nothing, er, nothing more I can add.'

Finch shifted his weight heavily onto his other foot. His balding head lowered itself across the patient and was now level with Katie Hobbs's frame. Katie was a smart girl. She had been paying attention. From my position at Katie's side, I could see that a major hospital incident was afoot if Katie got this wrong. He hadn't actually formulated a question yet, in fact I don't think he was going to, but he expected her to say something, all the same.

'Cigarettes, sir. Cigarette smoking. She forgot to mention cig—'

Finch did not allow Katie to finish. 'VICES!' he yelled at the top of his voice, so loud that the patient recoiled into the pillow. 'Bloody vices! The single most important thing. S-M-O-K-I-N-G,' then, quieter, '*smo*-king, boys and girls. *Smo*-king.'

That evening, back in my room, I reflected on the day's events. Sure, I had learnt something; we all had. But it somehow didn't seem fair to subject the patient to such an ordeal. He was dying in a lonely, soulless hospital ward with a growth that was enlarging daily in his chest cavity. His days were numbered, he knew that. Many years later, whilst looking after a wonderful Polish man with the same malignancy, I recalled the ward round and my mind had at once returned to the disquiet I'd felt in my room. Finch was just so *terrifying*. It's hard to cease turning over in one's head such troubled ruminations and I was surprised at how quickly, and vividly too, the churning process revisited my brain.

There could, I thought, be no defence of the way he was spoken to – no, spoken *about* – and it was wrong. I was mentally exhausted and fell asleep with a repetition of words chuntering through my cerebral hemispheres.

Heredity, sex and age, heredity sex and age, heredity sex and age...

The next day was spent in theatres. The seven of us changed into our greens and, with heavy white theatre boots on our feet, plonked our way to theatre number seven. Finch was waiting, scrubbed and impatient.

'You're late, you bunch of apes. Late.' Then turning to the theatre sister, a wisely woman who was accustomed to his truculent rants, he said, 'But that's their lookout, not mine. Right, Sister?' Sister nodded. 'Then we'll begin. Scalpel, Sister.'

November 1988. The train pulled into Waterloo station on a bleak morning. Most of the commuters headed for the 'drain', continuing their onward journey to the City, but I joined those queuing by the exit adjacent to Platform One. I walked through Lower Marsh Lane – known affectionately by the Lambethians as The Cut – and then through the maze of smaller roads that run alongside Archbishop's Palace. It was raining now but I didn't care; today was an important day. It was the day I finished Finch's Firm. I met Katie Hobbs by the lifts in the main hospital block. She was talking to Nabhi Shah, another member of our group. Nabhi was a confident, assertive chap who never let anyone or anything stand in his way. He had never let Finch intimidate him and not once did he appear ruffled by his unyielding discipline. I don't think he cared either way whether the firm was moving on or not.

'Hey, Mike!' he called out. 'We're on the Creamer and

Thompson Firm next but I haven't a clue where we're supposed to meet. I think it's outpatients.' He was right. The rest of the firm were waiting for us there. Adam Levy, the dentist, had already drawn up a time-table and now distributed copies to me, Katie Hobbs, Nabhi Shah, Becky Stratton, Philomena Tauber and Tania Peters. The clinic had already begun. Sir Richard Thompson, for he has since been knighted, is still a consultant at St Thomas's and highly regarded in the field of gastroenterology. Aloof, very bright and quick-witted, he was a proficient bedside teacher eager to impart his wisdom to students. Thompson is now physician to the Queen but, like most Oxford men, is quietly modest.

The 'other half' of the firm was with Dr Brian Creamer. Creamer had to be one of the best physicians that London had seen of late; by the time I joined his firm in 1988 he had been senior physician to the hospital for nearly thirty years. A kindly man, he was devoted to the hospital, to his staff and, above all, to his patients. He belonged to the old school: impeccably dressed, groomed and courteous. I learnt more medicine from him than from any other doctor and for this I shall be eternally grateful. He retired a year or so later, and his send-off was deservedly elaborate.

One evening a man arrived in casualty with severe

abdominal pain. He must have been in his sixties, but it was difficult to be sure as he was ashen grey with the pain which had imprinted itself onto his face by way of many furrowed wrinkles. He was, he said, a local fishmonger and had never before had a day's illness. The A&E doctor took a few details, conducted a cursory physical examination, and telephoned the duty surgeon.

'Got a chap here with acute pancreatitis. Done the amylase for you,' said the casualty officer. 'Result will be back in half an hour. He's all yours.'

Ten minutes later the patient is on a trolley and being pushed down the long central corridor of St Thomas's. Destination: surgical wards. Creamer is walking in the opposite direction, striding purposefully to his own ward at the other end of the hospital. The seven of us are following, like children following a teacher on a class outing. As the trolley passes by, Creamer steps to one side. As always, the perfect gentleman.

'Excuse me, porter! One minute!' says Creamer. 'Where are you taking this patient?'

The porter is surly and unfriendly. 'To the surgical ward. Gotta problem wi' that?'

'No,' replies Creamer, then quickly, 'but be so kind as to send him to my ward, please. Ninth floor, North Wing. There's a good chap.'

The porter huffs and lets out an exaggerated sigh.

Creamer turns to us, grinning, and taps his Mont Blanc fountain pen, which is peeping out of the top pocket of his starched white doctor's coat.

'We'll have some fun with this one,' he says. I am puzzled as to whether he means the patient or the writing instrument.

'What's with the pen, Dr Creamer?' ventures Nabhi Shah.

'You'll see,' says Creamer, and marches off. Obediently we follow, childlike but intrigued.

Later, gathered around the bedside, Creamer introduces us to his new patient. It's the man we had passed earlier in the corridor. Again I'm struck by the decency he shows the patient. Most patients have students thrust on them, guinea pigs upon whom nameless trainee doctors are encouraged to practise newly-acquired skills. Not so with Creamer.

The patient's pain has been eased by a painkilling injection and Creamer takes the man's hand in his own.

'Now, sir, I would very much like you tell me, and of course the students here, about your symptoms. Erm, Miss Peters. Would you like to ask some more questions about his pain?'

Tania asks whether the pain began suddenly or insidiously. Is it constant or intermittent? What factors aggravate it, or aren't there any? What about relieving factors? Does it lessen with a bowel movement? Or passing water? Does eating a meal help the pain, worsen it, or not make much difference? Is the pain colicky or knife-like? And so on. All the things we've been taught time and time again. And of course the time spent with Eric Finch ensured she has it off pat.

Creamer is pleased. It is clearly going well. He turns to the patient.

'Have you had any bleeding from the back passage, sir?' I like the way he chooses to address his patients. He *respects* them.

'Why yes. But I don't think I've mentioned it to anyone. Didn't think it was important.' The patient is clearly surprised that Creamer knows.

'Listen all of you,' says Creamer benevolently. 'He hasn't mentioned it because he damned well hasn't been asked. Now,' he says, facing the patient. 'Describe the bleeding.'

'Well it was, well ... you know, bleeding. It was blood.'

'I know, but what exactly did it *look* like?' Creamer urges the patient on and I know that this is leading somewhere, although where exactly I am not sure.

'It was dark, doc. Very dark.'

'Ah,' sighs Creamer knowingly. 'How dark?'

The patient pauses for just a second. 'Black,' he says.

Creamer reaches up to his pocket and with a flourish pulls out the Mont Blanc pen. It is the wide-barrelled sort, the fattest in the Mont Blanc range. He grips it betwixt his thumb and forefinger, as a gangster might a cigar, and holds it up so that it is level now with the patient's eyes.

'Like this? Was it as dark as this?'

A nod from the patient is all that Creamer needs. He spins around to face us and breaks into a wide grin.

'And *that*,' he says emphatically, 'is melaena.'

We returned to this patient several times over the next few days and Creamer explained the significance of melaena in reaching a diagnosis. It derives, he told us, from the Greek word *melas*, meaning 'black'. This is why we have melancholy, he said: sadness characterised by black moods of despair. Anyway, Creamer explained, if a patient passes blood from their back passage, the colour of the blood tells us from which part of the gut it originates. Blood from the anus is bright red and usually on the toilet tissue or coating the stool. Blood from the colon is darker: a rich plum colour and is mixed with the stool. But if a patient bleeds into their stomach, it takes a while for the blood to see daylight, as he put it, by which time it is very, very dark.

'Black, in fact. Melaena is black,' explained Creamer patiently. 'And so the diagnosis is simple. Abdominal pain and melaena can only equal one thing. Adam Levy, will you enlighten us?'

'Peptic ulcer?' replied Adam.

'Absolutely! Not acute pancreatitis. The casualty doctor was way off the mark! Take a proper history and the answers are always there. Staring you in the face. Just that, staring you in the face.'

4

In 1889, a junior anatomist at St Thomas's by the name of Parsons hit upon the idea of starting a newspaper for the hospital. He later recalled: 'it was in 79 Lambeth Palace Road, next door to the Two Sawyers, one November evening in 1889, that the idea first arose. I shared the house with Ernest Solly, the Surgical Registrar; and with us lived three or four resident pupils. The boys were by the fireside and one of them, J.L. Prain, looked up from a copy of the *Guy's Hospital Gazette* which he was reading and said to one of the other pupils: "Magpie! [the chap had earned the nickname for his talkativeness] Why shouldn't we have a gazette too? Shall you and I start one?"'

Parsons, who had overheard their conversation, thought this an excellent proposition provided, of course, that the hospital authorities consented to such a publication. Prain and his fellow pupil wished it to record the activities of the hospital's clubs and societies, but Parsons, who saw great potential to launch a noble hospital 'gazette', envisaged something far greater than just a sports magazine. He hoped for an unofficial record of the everyday life of the hospital from the students' point of view, edited and written by them, and kept as a memorial of their old companions and their days at St Thomas's. Most especially, Parsons reckoned on former students contributing articles to the *Gazette*, thereby making it a link between the hospital and those practitioners all over the world who had once belonged to it.

The first edition of the *St Thomas's Hospital Gazette* appeared in 1891 under the editorship of Dr F.G. Parsons. It rapidly became a well-respected journal, not just amongst the medical students and doctors but also amongst nurses, physiotherapists and other clinical personnel. It reflected every conceivable aspect of the lives of St Thomas's staff and students, and its pages contained a handsome mix of material: historical essays, clinical research papers and news of the hospital's clubs. The Editor was in sole charge of the publication, staying at the reins for as long as he (or she) wished, and handing over to a successor of his (or her!) own choosing.

The position of Editor was much coveted and I was therefore overjoyed when in 1989, one hundred years after Parsons had overheard Prain's remark to 'Magpie', I was chosen to edit the *Gazette*. I immediately set to work, gathering suitable newsworthy features, chasing up submissions half-promised to my predecessor, and identifying likely future contributors.

There was, thankfully, no shortage of quality copy material and it was gratifying that much of it came from the many and loyal St Thomas's alumni who were paid up subscribers to the *Gazette*. My postbag contained articles on subjects ranging from 'The Medical School in Wartime' (St Thomas's was badly damaged in the Second World War due to its close proximity to the Houses of Parliament) to 'General Practice in Queensland', the latter being one of many contributions that fulfilled the founding Editor's aspiration for the *Gazette* to serve as a link to St Thomas's men scattered throughout the world.

There were articles, too, on clinical matters: I printed a feature on osteopathy, another on varicose vein surgery, a discussion on home births, and a serious critique on medical ethics; the quality of authorship was high. There were also the by now obligatory reports from the many and diverse clubs at St Thomas's – the Medical and Physical Society, Football Club, Rugby Club (of course!), Croquet Club, Islamic Society and Paintball Club, to name but a few.

The same year that I assumed editorship of the *St Thomas's Hospital Gazette*, a Bill was submitted to Parliament to establish, by statute, the newly-merged medical schools of Guy's Hospital and St Thomas's Hospital. It was proposed that the new school be named the United Medical and Dental School of Guy's and St Thomas's Hospitals, an ugly and unwieldy mouthful which the majority of St Thomas's folk (and those at Guy's, too) came to detest. I was fearful for the future of the *Gazette* and arranged an urgent meeting with the medical school authorities. The Editor of *Guy's Hospital Gazette* had similar concerns and we held a joint meeting to argue our case. The Principal of 'UMDS' (the non-abbreviated title being far too cumbersome to reel off) was most reassuring. The *Gazettes* were safe, he assured us. I remember him raising an eyebrow to the Guy's chap, who said that if either magazine had to be axed then it should be the St Thomas's one as it was the 'younger' publication! The Principal, however, was emphatic: each was a tradition of their respective hospitals and as such *both* would stay.

So the *Gazette* continued, with each issue eagerly awaited by hospital staff and subscribers, many of whom wrote to me expressing their sense of relief that one of the last vestiges of St Thomas's Hospital had not disappeared in the merger with Guy's.

Nostalgia for the hospital was manifested in letters to the Editor. There was, for instance, a lively debate on the possessive form of the hospital's name. Correspondents were divided as to whether it should be *St Thomas's Hospital* or *St Thomas' Hospital*. The medical school, and the *Gazette*, shared my view that the apostrophe *s* (viz. St Thomas's Hospital) is correct but hospital staff disagreed: it is interesting that to this day there remain two 'official' versions: St Thomas' Hospital, the style that appears on hospital correspondence and documentation, and St Thomas's Hospital Medical School. I insisted that the *Gazette* retain the latter style as its loyalty was to the medical school (the source of its funding!). On this subject, it is noteworthy to quote *The Times Guide to English Style and Usage*, where special mention is made of this dissimilitude: 'Beware of organisations that have variations as their house style, eg, St Thomas' Hospital, where we must respect their whim.'

It was no easy task running the magazine single-handedly whilst attending to my studies, and more than once I was reminded of Parsons' own thoughts on this subject. He wrote:

A senior physician, for whom I had a great admiration, said to me: 'I think you're a fool, Parsons, not for starting this Gazette which, if wisely run, may do some good; but still a fool for allowing yourself to be made the Editor. You don't know what you're letting yourself in for, nor how many misunderstandings and misconstructions you are sure to encounter. Moreover, you find that having to provide a paper, month after month, in addition to your routine work, will sooner or later become a perfect nightmare and if you try to shuffle out of it, you will have done yourself and the School no good.'

How true!

In the physiology practical course, there was an 'experiment' (although the end point was already known, so there was nothing experimental about it) where we had to record the muscle contractions of a brain–dead frog. I say 'brain–dead' but this is a misnomer: we had first to insert a needle into the frog's neck and then wiggle it around in the spinal cord until we were satisfied that the poor creature was paralysed. Naturally, it was still alive but now, conveniently, it didn't writhe around when deep cuts were made in its legs. And there were plenty of frogs: one each, in fact.

Once the calf muscle – the gastrocnemius – had been identified, it was connected to a pressure transducer so that its contractions could be monitored. Various chemicals were then applied to the exposed muscle and the effect they had on the force or magnitude of each contraction was noted.

I considered the whole exercise barbaric and unnecessary: the same 'practical' had been part of the undergraduate course for so many years that my mother, who studied at St Thomas's thirty-two years before me, was not only able to describe the procedure and intended results, but even the actual laboratory, for this too hadn't changed. I just couldn't bring myself to partake in something so pointless, especially as we all knew what was supposed to happen.

I remember the professor of physiology, Anthony Taylor, snatching 'my' frog and performing the deed which I had refused to do, all the while muttering: 'Not cut out for this profession, students of today. Pathetic! Complete wimps!'

The muscle contractions were recorded by the movement of a needle (connected, in turn, to the transducer) on a drum coated with a layer of soot. But since we knew the supposed action of each chemical substance, we fudged the results accordingly. This was easy enough to accomplish by a little jog of the needle on the drum, but first the drum must be re-smoked otherwise there were would be a tell-tale sign of a double trace. There is, of course, a limit to this, the perfect being the enemy of the reasonably good.

I had not appreciated just how practised the tradition of fudging the Frog Practical results were until the *Gazette* office received a wonderful account, written in verse, of what could happen if the experiment had to be performed under examination conditions. It illustrates the risk inherent in any form of scientific cheating, namely that of having no result at all.

PHYSIOLOGY (1928)

The old man sighed, then raised his frail head,
Bestirred himself before the final sleep;
And to the waiting friends around him said:
'Into mine errant mind unwanted creep
Thoughts of things I've left undone,
Thoughts of prizes never won,
Thoughts of books I never read,
Thoughts of things I never said,
Thoughts of life lived half unlived.'
He paused and sank into a troubled sleep,
Then rose again the fire in his eye –
'Time yet there is,' he said. 'I will fulfill
My youthful promises most faithfully.
I will rise up from my bed,
I will say those things unsaid,

I will purge myself of sin,
I a maid will woo and win,
I will have a little son,
I will do those things undone,
I will live that life unlived.'
Into the cluster round about the bed,
Came Death in awful majesty sublime,
And echoing through that chamber of the dead,
Went failure's grim last words:
Re-smoke drum ... 'TIME!'

In the fiftieth anniversary issue of the *Gazette*, which appeared in 1941 when the hospital had evacuated from war-time London, Parsons wrote:

After six years as Editor, I gave the post into other hands, feeling sure that the *Gazette* was now firmly established and doing useful work for the Hospital and School. I could not, of course, foresee that after fifty years of life it would be stronger and more vigilant than ever, nor did I dream that its jubilee would be celebrated while St Thomas's was so sorely stricken as to be almost deserted. I cheer the *Gazette* as it begins its second half century.

We can be sure that Dr Parsons would have applauded the elegant centenary edition of *St Thomas's Hospital Gazette*, produced by my successor in 1991, the year of my leaving St Thomas's. But the *Gazette*, sadly, could not hold its own under the hospital's amalgamation with Guy's, and when UMDS was itself swallowed up by King's College in that final act of pitiful surrender, I knew that her days were numbered.

The autumn 1996 issue of the *St Thomas's Hospital Gazette* rolled off the press at Port Talbot just two weeks before Roopal gave birth to our first child. The cover is characteristically vibrant and bold: this time a collage of colourful photographs depicts undergraduate teaching at St Thomas's. The tone is upbeat: there is even an invitation on page five for readers to become involved in the *Gazette*'s production, and an advertisement for its new website. The editorial makes no mention of the fact that this is to be the last issue of my beloved journal. The ignominious decision by the medical school authorities, or perhaps it was the Principal himself, to pull the plug on the *Gazette* so suddenly was cowardly; there was no subsequent edition in which to publish the hundreds of letters, as I am sure there must have been, from outraged alumni determined to keep the torch flame burning for their noble *alma mater*.

The death rattle had truly sounded for more than one hundred years of literary history. I feel proud to have been a part of it.

5

Christmas in London is fabulous and 1989 was no different. On most days in December, as soon as my ward duties had finished, I would leave the cosseted but stuffy confines of the hospital and exhilarate in the cold, biting wind as I crossed the Thames at Westminster. At Parliament Square I would wander towards Westminster Cathedral or perhaps stroll up Whitehall. London is a city of contrasts, a melting pot of cultures, tastes and peoples. And it never ceases to amaze how our capital has produced roads so different, so diverse. I would walk through The Cut twice every day, and yet north of the river I would find a labyrinth of streets far removed from the sights and sounds of Lambeth. I would return to St Thomas's, re-crossing the river at Waterloo Bridge and walking down Embankment in front of the magnificent County Hall building.

After New Year we joined another firm, and then another, and so on; in this way we managed to see the diseases of all the major specialties. Modern medicine has eradicated many diseases that were once common in

Britain (I have never seen a case of measles or leprosy or acute syphilis, for example) but are still encountered by doctors practising in Third World communities.

Medical students are encouraged to travel abroad in order to see how clinical practice compares in a country other than Britain. But where to go? I paired up with a fellow student and friend, Mark Grainger, and we sat in the library late one Tuesday evening, poring over a file crammed with 'write-ups' by our predecessors.

'Hey! Look at this!' said Mark, holding up a sheet of foolscap paper. It was headed 'Nairobi – an elective spent bumming all day and much of the night'. He began to read aloud: 'On our elective trip we decided the best approach was to do no work and have a f***ing good time. There weren't any patients as the hospital had relocated following a fire the year before, and anyway...'

'Oh come on, Mark,' I said. 'There must be *something...*'

'Yeah, only joking,' he said. 'What about this?'

He had pulled out a detailed report by a couple of students who had visited India three years previously. He read it and then passed it across to me.

Seven weeks later we were on an aeroplane bound for Bangalore, arriving by car at the town of Madanapalle a few hours later. A couple of miles to the west is a small village called Arogyavaram, meaning the 'gift of health'. There we worked in a tuberculosis sanitorium for a couple of months, looking after inpatients and attending out-patient clinics; Mark and I saw more physical signs (of illness) at Arogyavaram than in five years spent at medical school in London.

This was as well, for in summer the following year I sat 'finals' – both written and oral examinations in medicine, paediatrics, surgery, obstetrics, gynaecology and thera-peutics. In the run-up to the exams I scoured every corner of the hospital in search of valuable 'clinical material' – aka patients – on whom I would practise my clinical skills. If it moved it had a stethoscope placed on its chest, an auriscope poked in each ear, and two hundred and four blows (from one hundred and two tendon hammers) by the medical school's final year contingent. The patients were fed up; we were fed up; and I was exhausted. In the end it was damned well impossible for the examiners to find suitable patients to use for the examinations. Even the hospital's star patient – a lady with Klippel-Trenauney-Weber syndrome (I won't begin to explain this one!) – had been seen by every student several times over. Legend has it that some years ago a hospital circumvented this difficulty by placing paper bags over the hapless patients' heads.

It was clear that something had to be done and so they

came up with the idea of sending us to other London medical schools. I had friends at most of these schools and quickly made a list of their names and telephone numbers. The plan was to telephone them as soon as I knew where I was to be sent. You can almost imagine the conversation.

'Oi! Fred! What you got at Bart's now?'

'You know, usual stuff. A few dozen heart attacks and oodles of old dears with pneumonia.'

'No, not that sort! You know they can't put anyone who's ill into the exams in case they peg it. Wouldn't look good. No – come on, the fancy crap.'

'Well, there's a bloke with cerebral sarcoidosis…'

'Oh bloody hell, I don't know the first thing about that. How will I know if it's him?'

'That's easy, Michael, easy. He's about forty – no, a bit older. Average height, average build. Black moustache – no, wait! The nurse shaved it off yesterday on the consultant's instructions as he might be used in the exam. A bit shifty-looking, 'tho that's probably because every Bart's student has been to see him a zillion times.'

No, it would never work. In any case, the examiners were wise to such hanky panky. They had us report to the Dean's Office at 9 a.m. and gave us our marching orders. No time to ask the audience or, literally, phone a friend. You either knew your stuff or … failed.

I was told to be at Charing Cross Hospital in Fulham by 10 a.m. I met Brian Creamer in the main central corridor, not far from our encounter with the porter and the melaena patient. If only the examination case could be something like that, I thought.

Charing Cross is an ugly and unimaginitive block of concrete and grey metal, set amongst rows of one-time workers' cottages which now are desirable residences for journalists and city folk. I found my way to the examination centre and was introduced to Justin, a cheeky and healthy-looking seven-year-old boy. His mother sat by his side whilst he did cartwheels on the bed.

'I know what's wrong with him but they told me not to tell you,' she said.

Oh thanks, I thought. I'll return the favour some day.

I asked all the usual questions, first of her, then Justin, then her again.

'So you say there's nothing wrong?' I implored. There must be, I thought, otherwise what the bloody hell is he doing here?

'Nope. He's fine,' said Justin's mother, clutching her son's Action Man.

'Are you sure? Does he attend a special clinic here, for instance?'

She paused. 'He used to,' she conceded, 'but not any more.'

At last. 'What clinic was that?' I asked.

'Oh I couldn't tell you.'

'Have you forgotten?'

'No,' she said slowly. 'I'm not allowed to tell you anything, remember?'

Aaaghh!

I cajoled her, pleaded with her, begged her. But nothing. Absolutely nothing.

The bell rang after seven minutes and I knew I was doomed.

The professor of paediatrics, a fat chap with half-moon spectacles, strode in with his right hand proffered from half way across the room. He smiled – superficially, I thought – and then winked at the boy, as if to say: Well, you've met another buffoon who's going to fail.

The professor indicated a chair at a long table and after I was seated he took up his position opposite me. His chair had leather side-arms whereas mine didn't; funny the things one notices under duress. His co-examiner, nameless and so far unspeaking, sat by his side.

'So, Young Doctor Sir,' said the fat professor. 'Perhaps you would like to present your findings.' He smiled a weak smile.

And so I began the speech of a condemned man. I did not have any findings. There weren't any, sir, I explained. Justin's mother, I told him, said he was well. I wanted to ask the examiners if it was a trick. Had they put a well patient in the exam to catch me out? Watching a red-faced student struggle through the examination of a pregnant woman and then asking him to determine her gestation. And which way up, would you say, is the baby? Enjoying the torture and then, Ha ha ha, she's not pregnant at all. Just overweight! But this wasn't a joke. The professor was serious.

He looked at me and I looked at him. I turned to the co-examiner. Nothing, not even an acknowledgement, just a cold, empty stare.

'Well then, I'd better enlighten you,' he said. 'He has Weber syndrome.'

I knew very little about this and almost certainly not enough to make up for my disastrous performance. Weber syndrome results in paralysis of the muscles that moves *one* of the eyes, a drooping lid over the same eye and, confusingly, weakness – sometimes even paralysis – of the arm and leg on the *opposite* side. This took all of ten seconds to say.

The examiners weren't impressed.

'And who was Weber?' Ah! The co-examiner has a voice after all.

Ask me another, I wanted to say. I had told them all I knew of Weber syndrome.

'Erm. He was a physician at the turn of the century, sir.' This is a stock answer to such questions and for one awful minute I feared that the man who had just asked the question might be Weber himself. Imagine! I felt my pulse race and my mouth go even drier. I longed for a glass of water and the chance to escape.

'Sounds about right,' murmured the quiet one.

'What do you suppose is the aetiology of this condition?' It was the professor who was now leading the questions. Blimey, I didn't have the faintest idea. Through the grimy, rain-spotted window I could see the BBC Television Centre in Wood Lane. Why, I thought, do most consultants assume this air of superiority? The 'big I am' attitude. Why? Why not behave like us mortals?

My mind drifted back to the start of my clinical years and Eric Finch. You ignorant bunch of thickies, he would chide. And there was his rhyme...

Hey! That was it! That was really it.

> *Heredity, sex and age,*
> *Occupation, race and clime,*
> *The ills that men are subject to –*
> *The vices of our time.*

Here goes, I thought. Look confident and it might just work. You've got nothing to lose, mate.

I took a deep breath. 'It's long been recognised that heredity plays a very significant part in the aetiology of Weber's,' I bluffed, omitting 'syndrome' in the hope that this would suggest confidence and familiarity with the disease. Who nowadays says diabetes mellitus? Plain old diabetes is the norm.

'It's more prevalent in boys,' I continued. This was a shot in the dark but I reckoned that as Justin, the patient before me, was male I had a better than average chance of being right.

'Carry on, carry on,' said the professor.

'As for age, it … it can occur at any age. But it's more common with … *advancing* years.' *Most things are.* Very few conditions become less likely as one ages.

And so it continued. I bungled my way through occupation, racial origin and climate. I made some comment on predisposing illness and, finally, on whether cigarettes and alcohol had a part to play in the causation of this confounded disease.

And that was it.

It was over.

My father is a paediatrician. That evening, on the telephone, he delighted in telling me all there is to know about Weber and his blessed syndrome. Weber, he told me, was born in 1823, the son of a German father and Italian mother. He grew up in Bavaria and studied medicine in Bonn. He was crazy about Shakespeare and, realising that the Bard's plays sound better in their native language, set about learning English. He emigrated to Britain, where he took up a post at Guy's Hospital and married an English girl. He was a charming, amiable sort of chap who easily gathered a circle of folk around him; he would tell story upon story to an audience quite mesmerised.

It was Weber who first suggested that British patients with tuberculosis should be sent to a cold environment such as Switzerland, and he penned many articles on this treatment, which became known as 'climatotherapy'. He was knighted and died in 1918.

'But dad,' I said when he'd finished the mini-biography, 'this boy I examined. The one who was meant to have Weber's. He looked completely normal. I don't understand.'

'Ah, yes,' said my father, 'that may be so, but did you *really* examine him? I mean properly. Get him to walk to see if there was any motor weakness. Get him to sit still while you looked for abnormality in his eyes. Did you?'

I thought about the little blighter jumping up and down on the hospital bed, trampolining while I was taking the most important examination of my entire life. Thanks, sonny. Thanks to you I have screwed up my finals. No sooner had the thought entered my head than I felt remorse; a bad doctor shouldn't blame his patients. If he cannot elicit a physical sign then he has only himself to blame.

Justin *must* have had a weakness down one side of his body and I failed to spot it. *Mea culpa* and no excuses.

Two weeks later, on a hot and sticky June afternoon, I had a telephone call from Adam Levy. 'They'll be on the noticeboard in an hour or so. D'ya want to walk over with me?'

We met on Lambeth Palace Road. I had bumped into Becky Stratton and Katie Hobbs in The Cut, and together we sauntered over to the Dean's Office. There were students milling expectantly around the bare noticeboard. Leaning against the wall which separates the hospital's grounds from the Embankment below was Nabhi Shah, a can of Coke passing intermittently to his lips, indifferent, relaxed, cool-headed. Above him, from its position across the river, Big Ben chimed the hour. I cannot remember which hour, possibly three, maybe four o'clock, but the words of Virginia Woolf come to mind: 'A particular hush, or solemnity; an indescribable pause; a suspense before Big Ben strikes. There! Out it boomed. First a warning, musical; then the hour, irrevocable.'

My mother had stood in this same spot years before and she too had been subjugated by Big Ben's timely domination. And now with the reverberation of the final dong hanging over and around us, I became distracted by a ripple of activity within the assembled throng as a woman emerged from Block 8 of the South Wing. Held up in front of her bust, like Oliver Twist's proffered bowl, was a sheet of white foolscap paper. The crowd parted with unusual politeness, thereby allowing her to reach the board. She pinned the sheet by each of its corners, using new, shining drawing pins.

She did this slowly and very carefully, not letting herself be hurried by the crowd around her. Her deed done, she set off briskly to return whence she'd come.

I had passed.

6

I left Kingston Hospital at the end of July 1992. I'd kept my mouth shut and emerged triumphant, waving the two precious slips of paper that I duly sent to the General Medical Council. Now I was a doctor in *every* sense of the word. I could write prescriptions for non-hospitalised patients and certify deaths. It was with this newly acquired status that I looked around for another job.

In October that year I accepted a post as a junior psychiatrist to West Park Hospital. An old Victorian establishment, it was one of the last true lunatic asylums built in the late 1890s to house the insane. It was surrounded by acres of beautiful parkland, much of it overgrown when I worked there; I did not like the place for it was creepy, and I would shudder as I drove through the large and blackened wrought-iron gates that marked the hospital's entrance from the main road. The main building was another couple of hundred yards or so from these gates but the short journey along the shingled narrow driveway always signified much more to me. It represented the passage from a world resplendent with energy and happiness, to one which finds solace in misery, melancholy and, as much as I hate the word, madness.

Generations ago, young people had been sent there on the slightest 'charge'. Many a time, whilst writing in a patient's case notes, I would turn the pages back to entries made perhaps fifty or more years earlier. Here I would find, in copperplate handwriting, the particulars pertaining to the patient's admission.

May 1938. Aged 16. Admitted to West Park Lunatic Asylum for misdemeanor. Seen behaving inappropriately with village boy. Girl's father local JP. Matter discussed with said father. He distraught by his daughter's flirtations. Recommended action: admission to hospital for respite care and formal supervision.

October 1943. Aged 24. Admitted to West Park Lunatic Asylum for imbecilic activity. Stole fruit from market — apprehended by police constable. Upon questioning etc spat at aforementioned police constable and laughed. General Practitioner called to examine, and declared man of unsound mind. Doctor advised admission to West Park. This recommendation accepted as valid by West Park resident medical officer.

I felt enormous shame upon reading these ancient case histories. I was a resident medical officer and it tormented me to think that predecessors of mine had been instrumental in ruining young lives – not just many of the seven hundred souls then at West Park but the hundreds of others in psychiatric institutions around the country. Not long ago Britain was still littered with crumbling Victorian mental hospitals and it is only recently that great effort has been put into effectively resettling their long-term residents into the community; the Government's White Paper on a new Mental Health Act which came out in December 2000 had, as its key element, compulsory care in the community.

As a senior house officer (SHO), I was responsible for the care of long-term patients at West Park, the majority of whom had not set foot outside the hospital for fifty years. Labels, for that is the only word I can use to describe them, such as 'imbecile' or 'insane' or 'person of unsound mind' had been entered in their case histories: diagnoses they were not, for surely no doctor could justify their use – let alone pass them off as clinical terms.

The residents' close relatives had died, or at any rate stopped visiting for whatever reason, and they had become socially neglected and forgotten. Worse, they were institutionalised. This disturbed me beyond measure.

They had been admitted whilst young, and doubtless proclaimed their innocence with a vehemence possessed only by the sane, but after a while each would realise that to argue with authority was pointless; in forlorn recognition that he or she was destined to stay, the new 'patient' would adopt the behaviour of the truly insane.

Not just the behaviour, but mannerisms too, and all the other quirks of a deranged and befuddled mind. Their thought processes became disordered, and their ability to relate and to communicate disappeared forever. The most poignant part of all this, I remember thinking, was that they had assumed the bizarre cerebration not of a kosher psychiatric patient but that of a fellow long-serving inmate. Imagine how it must have been for a cocky, ill-disciplined, rebellious perhaps, but completely sane young man to have found himself incarcerated in the gloomy confines of somewhere like West Park Hospital.

Some hospital, I often told myself in those first few months. Where was the treatment? There was no attempt by the doctors to heal. Don't fret, lad, the kindly psychiatrist would say. You can turn over a new leaf here. Make a new start. That's the ticket, lad. Show us and your family that you've mended your ways, and you'll be discharged soon enough. Yes, the psychiatrist would soothe, you'll be out of here in a couple of years.

The patient would rebel against the orderlies who bring his meals. Tell them he's done nothing wrong. Become surly and taciturn. After a few months his parents would lengthen the interval between their visits until they ceased coming altogether. That's not our boy in there, they would remark. Look at him! He's changed. It was the right thing sending him into West Park, they would say in relief.

Their beloved son had indeed changed. His rebelliousness had softened now and he was embracing the aura of those who had been at West Park for years before him. They too had once been normal. Now they were hopeless and helpless and mad. Those that followed them, like our lad and those after him, followed suit. A tragic waste of life.

I was responsible too for referrals from local general practitioners and from doctors working in the A&E at Epsom Hospital. Most of the referrals concerned depressed folk who were threatening suicide or who had already taken an overdose. The majority came my way during the night, which meant leaving the cosy safety of the on-call doctor's accommodation and driving to the general hospital – at Epsom – a couple of miles away. I became a familiar figure in A&E and was known by the emergency staff as 'the psychiatrist', an image I later found difficult to shrug off.

One Saturday evening in November 1992, I received a telephone call from a Dr Bonner-Morgan, a competent and well-respected GP, who had visited a sixty-seven-year-old man by the name of Ted Leonard. Leonard's neighbours were worried about his recent behaviour and had asked his GP to call on him. Their concern was justified, Bonner-Morgan explained to me on the telephone, for Mr Leonard was imagining the presence of strangers within his house. Bonner-Morgan thought an urgent psychiatric assessment was indicated.

'But this is common, isn't it?' I reasoned. 'Elderly folk often imagine that people have been in their house. All part of early dementia –'

'Yes,' interrupted Bonner-Morgan, 'but this man isn't elderly. He's only sixty-seven. And what's more,' he continued, 'he can actually see them now, whilst I'm in his house.'

I had to agree that this was unusual. The type of paranoid thoughts that lead the elderly to believe that someone has been in their house almost always occur when they are alone, particularly at night. Dr Bonner-Morgan was right: this chap needed to come in.

I loathed the oppressive and heavy air that hung over

West Park and I knew that if I admitted Mr Leonard to my ward there, his mind would fester and his brain rot. I had at my disposal a handful of beds in the main hospital at Epsom, testimony to the already-changing status of psychiatric care. Here we would put teenagers who had taken overdoses, housewives who were suffering an acute stress reaction, and business executives who had suddenly become manic.

So it was here, away from the empty yet troubled gazes of those languishing at West Park, that I admitted Ted Leonard. His story gave me a fascinating insight into the mind of someone tormented by visual hallucinations.

'Dr Bonner-Morgan tells me you're aware of people visiting your house?' I had to start somewhere and this seemed as good a place as any.

'No, Dr Barrie,' countered Mr Leonard. His ability to remember my name, having presumably been told it by the ward receptionist, was not consistent with an aging brain. 'I'm not just aware of my visitors, I can see them. They're very real, I can tell you.'

Mr Leonard glanced cautiously around the interview room. 'I have to keep my voice down,' he continued in a whisper. 'They might be listening.'

'Why? Are they in here?'

'No. But you never know. So far I have only seen them

in my house. They...' Mr Leonard looked up and I nodded, indicating that he should go on.

'They ... well, let's just say that they are very, *very* shifty. Unbelievably so. I wouldn't put it past them to come here.'

'Tell me about them, Mr Leonard.' I added the date to a sheet of plain A4 paper and got ready to write some notes.

'Well, where to begin, eh?' smiled Leonard, amused by his own rhetoric.

And so it was that over the next hour and a half he recounted his story. He remembered the day when, some five months earlier, he had confronted two Indian men seated on the sofa in his living room.

'They were deep in conversation,' he recalled. 'Didn't stop talking or so much as look at me when I entered the room. I shouted "Hey, what's going on in here? Who are you?"

'I wasn't frightened, just angry. The impudence of it all. And d'you know what? They ignored me. Just kept chatting to each other. I couldn't actually hear what they were saying, mind you. Every now and then they looked up at me, but talking the whole while. They kept this up for about twenty minutes and then got up and walked out.'

'Where did they walk out?' I asked. 'I mean, *how* did they leave?'

'Well, through the door, of course. How else would they leave?' Leonard seemed astonished at my ignorance.

'And that was that,' he continued. 'But the next day the same two men returned. This time they were joined by another guy — he arrived ten minutes or so later — and then all three left together. Strange, because *he's* never come again. I mean the other two are regulars, but I've never seen the third chap again.

'Well, this carried on for several days; each time the first two would be joined by one or two other men, and they would all leave together. I must have seen twenty new faces, and then a peculiar thing happened.

'One day the two men were sitting on my sofa as usual. I'd gone upstairs to fetch something and when I re-entered my living room the two of them were there. You know, the same two from the first day. After a while the door opened and I looked up, expecting to see yet another new face. But this time the man that entered was one of the guys that had come before. It's strange but I can honestly say that no new stranger has come since this time. There's always a third or fourth man, but he's one of the twenty or so who have been before. They enjoy it, you see.'

'Enjoy what?'

'Keeping me in suspense, of course! They've introduced the clan to me — well, if you can call *that* introducing oneself — and now they want me to guess who the additional member's going to be. They just jabber away the whole time but I can't hear a word of it, obviously.'

'Why?' I was intrigued.

'Oh, I'm sorry, I thought I told you. When they talk I just see their lips move, like on silent films. And they're all Indian or Pakistani or whatever. I am not sure which.'

Blimey, this was complex! Hallucinations are the province of those with mental illnesses: schizophrenia, drug-induced psychosis, dementia. But all of these cause blunting of cognitive function so that the hallucinations inevitably assume a pretty basic form. A voice in one's head perhaps, or seeing Winston Churchill standing at the end of the bed. But Mr Leonard was far from mentally blunt. His mind was agile and his so-called disordered perception had every sense of order.

His hallucinations formed a complex system where 'intruders' effectively worked a rota as to when they would visit and speak — or at least move their lips. Leonard didn't exhibit the confused mind or self-neglect of an untreated schizophrenic, and I couldn't elicit anything to suggest he was depressed. He denied drug abuse and clearly wasn't dementing. He lacked insight. After all, he was convinced that the strangers were real.

I pondered the history that Mr Leonard gave. The more I heard, the more uneasy I became. What if he were right? Maybe he was the victim of some awful conspiracy and, despite his protestations that he'd witnessed people in his house, I was about to lock him up in a psychiatric ward. I felt a lump in the back of my throat as it dawned on me: he *really* was seeing intruders in his house.

'Mr Leonard,' I interrupted.

Leonard stopped mid-sentence and looked up, a weak smile on his face.

'I'm sorry. I must have bored you with all that detail.'

'No, no. But tell me something, please. Have you ever seen these intruders outside?'

'Never.' He was emphatic.

'Are you sure?'

'Absolutely.'

'Are there any in this room? Look carefully.'

Mr Leonard laughed. 'Dr Barrie, I'm telling you I haven't seen them outside my house. Although, as I've said, I wouldn't put it past them to come and watch me here.' Leonard gave a little shudder at this unpleasant thought.

I explained the admission procedure to him and then

returned to the doctor's accommodation at West Park. I was troubled by his presentation and his vehemence that what he had seen was real. Outside I could see the bedraggled inhabitants of the hospital, aimlessly shuffling around the grounds. The same innocents whose admission to this hospital I had lamented. Like Mr Leonard, they had protested their innocence but to no avail. Their minds, bright at the time of their wrongful incarceration, eroded by years of non-stimulation: empty now and vacant.

I thought of Eric Finch at St Thomas's and how he'd insisted that every set of symptoms be packaged into a diagnosis. What kind of stupid doctor, I could imagine Finch shouting, would prescribe medication without having made a diagnosis? How can you give a drug which is specifically licensed for a disease, if you haven't yet diagnosed it? Fools! he would chide, fools practise this way.

I decided to drive straight back to Epsom.

Leonard was sitting on his bed, fidgeting nervously with the strap on his wristwatch. He sat up as I approached. I asked him if he had seen any of the strange visitors after I'd left him. No, he said.

'Could you describe their clothes for me? Do they wear suits?'

'Of course not, I mean they couldn't really. You see they haven't got any legs.'

I cursed myself for not having asked the right questions to have extracted this earlier. Leonard explained that he could see their faces and torsos and even their feet, but that their legs appeared to be missing.

I cannot describe my feelings of relief. I made my way back to West Park and lay down on my narrow bed. *Thank you Eric*, I whispered. *Thank you.*

Leonard remained at Epsom for almost three weeks, during which time I spent many hours going over his incredible story time and again. I was fascinated by the complexity of his hallucinations – as thankfully I now knew them to be – but also by the fact that for him they remained intensely vivid. The paranoid delusions and hallucinations of those with dementia quickly fade as the brain function deteriorates further, as, too, do the perceptual distortions experienced by psychotics. Yet Leonard was ever-suspicious and on his guard lest 'they' – as he now referred to his Indian visitors – returned.

One morning on the ward I heard a nurse cry out for assistance. I ran over to the main dormitory section to find her restraining Leonard. She had managed to grab the patient's arms – but Leonard was clearly agitated and his expression conveyed fear. He was punching the air in front of him, and made no attempt to push the nurse either away or off him. I approached to one side and asked Leonard what was the matter.

'They've come for me, doc. I knew they would. Look!'

I realised it would be futile to deny their existence as this would upset the man further and create yet more tension. The situation seemed now to be under control; the nurse had calmed Leonard and his hallucinations were abating.

I was determined to figure out what the diagnosis was. Apart from hallucinations, he displayed none of the so-called 'first rank' symptoms of schizophrenia, and in any case it is rare for someone to develop this late in life.

What about dementia? Alzheimer's? I turned the matter over and over in my head many times and yet the more I thought about it, the more I was troubled. Leonard was on my mind at work, in the car and at home.

Roopal was wonderful when I explained the dilemma to her and she saw the problem I faced. How can a doctor cure a patient if he doesn't have a diagnosis? She also saw the solution, or rather a means to find it. 'St Thomas's,' was all she said back in our flat in Surbiton. We'd bought a small flat in a cul-de-sac called Waterside Close, although the only water to be found was the rain water which collected in the puddles in the courtyard outside.

But it was home, our first home in fact, and we were comfortable and happy.

'What's St Thomas's got to do with any of this?' I asked.

'That's where you went to learn, so it's there that you must now return to find your answers.' I knew that Roopal was right. I would find a diagnosis for Ted Leonard at my *alma mater*.

I returned to St Thomas's Hospital Medical School on a warm Saturday morning a few days later; sweeping nostalgia and with it the temptation to reminisce aside, I climbed the single flight of stairs that led to the library.

Outside, Big Ben marked time. As a student I'd become so accustomed to her famous chimes but today, a day of rare and beautiful sunshine, I heard every damn bell strike. *Ding dong dang dong, dong dang ding dong* – *DONG DONG DONG*… The final 'dongs', counting the hours, were carried across the calm ebb of the Thames to where I sat, taunted and mocked by their intrusion. I felt belittled, foolish even, to be stuck inside an academic library when I could be enjoying my free time outside.

I surrounded myself with dozens upon dozens of specialist texts. Not just the generalist tomes by authors whose boast it is that theirs covers the myriad of psychiatric conditions in their entirety, but material –

reference works and journals and abstracts – dealing specifically with perceptual disorders of the mind.

I read about Othello syndrome, where the patient has a delusion that his spouse is unfaithful; Capgras syndrome, the delusion that a close relative has been replaced by an exact double; and Fregoli syndrome, the delusion that individuals familiar to the patient have disguised themselves to appear as others. Elsewhere I read about de Clérambault syndrome, the fascinating condition where a person becomes convinced that a complete stranger is in love with him (or her!), and other equally intriguing eponymous psychiatric disorders.

Each new book I opened seemed to detail a psychiatric condition of which I had previously been ignorant, and this made me even more determined in my quest to get to the root of Leonard's visual hallucinations.

One book concentrated on delusions and hallucinations purely of a visual nature. There was a lengthy case history of a blind man who held an unshakeable belief that he could see. Of course he could not: but he was deluded that he could. The text's author explained this was Anton syndrome. I read on.

Blimey! The words on the next page made my heart miss a beat. Roopal had been right! Seek and ye shall find. It was like a key opening a lock and the fit was perfect:

Ted Leonard must have a disease called Charles Bonnet syndrome.

Charles Bonnet was a Swiss philosopher in the eighteenth century who was intrigued by his grandfather's visions of birds and buildings that others could not see. The grandfather had been blinded by cataracts and Bonnet realised that the visions, which were figments of the grandfather's imagination, had not been present prior to him going blind. Charles Bonnet syndrome, as it came to be known, describes the phenomena of visual hallucinations in those with poor eyesight. The visions can take the form of simple patterns or, as in Leonard's case, complex images of people. The hallucinations can be pleasurable or upsetting.

Charles Bonnet syndrome only affects those with sight loss and usually occurs in later life. For reasons not fully understood, the hallucinations are more prominent when the patient is alone and when the light is poor, for example at dusk when one relies on failing daylight and hasn't yet switched a light on.

Most sufferers keep their symptoms quiet for fear of being considered insane or demented. Perhaps this is why I had not previously heard of this condition. One book gave an account of a patient's hallucinations not too dissimilar from my own patient back at Epsom:

Although the visions themselves may not be frightening, it is disturbing to start seeing strangers in your home. We looked after one man who had visions of numerous tiny people, all wearing a strange costume. He described them as similar to elves, except more human-like. The man would confront these tiny people by saying 'Right. What have you got in store for me today?' The strangers in his house would, of course, not answer him.

It was a Saturday but I was too excited to wait until Monday to pursue matters back at Epsom. I crossed Lambeth Palace Road outside the A&E department and headed up Royal Street. After a few minutes I was in The Cut. It was market day and I pushed my way through the throngs of shoppers, eager in my rush to reach Waterloo Station. The station had changed since I'd last seen it, as a final-year student in 1991, for work had begun on the construction of the new international terminal for Eurostar.

I reached the station entrance and found the right platform for the fast train to Epsom. I thought, with some irony, how much clearer the signal board appeared and realised it was because I now wore spectacles! With hindsight, things had been blurred toward the end of my medical training and yet I'd been ignorant then of both my own need for glasses and the very condition that would cause me to come back in order to find out more.

When finally I reached Epsom the sun had retreated over the top of the Downs, and the trees on the Dorking Road cast long shadows as I walked from the station to the hospital. It was still warm when I entered the psychiatric ward. Leonard was sitting alone, dejected and forlorn.

'They've been watching me the past couple of days, especially at this time of evening,' he explained. 'See over there? That's where new ones come in.' Leonard pointed to an interconnecting door at the side of the ward.

'Are there any here now?' I asked.

'Oh yes,' said Leonard. He nodded his head to an area a few feet in front of him, and then went on to say how today they'd been plotting to kill him. He said that they had shown him the knife they intended to use. 'But I don't think they will risk doing it with you here, doctor, as they could be charged in your presence as a witness.'

I told Leonard how I thought we might be able to help him. He was sceptical but happy to cooperate with my proposed treatment.

On Monday I arranged for a full optical and orthoptic and ophthalmological assessment. Leonard wore spectacles already but these were exchanged for state–of–the–art lenses with the ability to refract to even greater clarity.

Examination of his retinae unfortunately revealed age-related macular degeneration, which, as the name suggests, is part of the aging process and can be neither cured nor halted.

For three weeks the hallucinations disappeared. Every day I would ask Leonard if he'd had any sightings and, beaming, he would report that he had not. The response to his improved vision was so good that I discharged him.

I went to visit him three months later and all was fine. By six months, however, the visual hallucinations had returned and so I arranged an urgent appointment with the ophthalmologist. Leonard's macular degeneration had worsened and this was undoubtedly the cause of his relapse. I could think of nothing that might help; Leonard was opposed to my offer of hospital admission as he realised that on this occasion it would be to West Park, where he would likely remain as a life-long resident.

In an attempt to lessen the fear of his hallucinations, he now turned on all the lights as the evenings drew close, especially in winter, and somewhat poignantly had taken to keeping a golf club by his armchair so that he could retaliate if attacked.

★   ★   ★

A few months later I traded the besuited attire of a psychiatrist for the shirt sleeves of a paediatrician. My successor took the reins of the mental health unit, and I handed over to him all those who had been under my care both at Epsom and West Park. When I had begun there were nine hundred patients at West Park Hospital but now there were seven hundred. A few had died but many had been rehoused in the community following the Government's Care in the Community Bill.

A year or so after I left, there were only a handful of patients still at West Park, the ones whom the authorities were finding it hard to place in the utterly unsuitable outside world. Before long they too had gone, unready and unprepared, into a society that had changed far more than they had over the preceding fifty or sixty years. The deserted hospital was bulldozed to make way for new housing – hundreds of new properties crammed into the once-sprawling site.

A friend of mine, he was the best man at my wedding, has bought one of the new houses on the site, and the hairs on my back rise whenever I visit him. The place holds too many memories and for me the ghosts will shuffle along those drafty corridors in eternity.

I do not know what became of Ted Leonard.

7

Epsom Hospital employed three junior paediatricians at senior house officer (SHO) level. They, together with four consultants, made up the children's department. That was it; no registrars – the so-called 'middle grade' doctors. Things weren't too bad during the day for if I got stuck on a difficult problem I could always ask one of the four consultants who invariably would be found in the outpatient clinic or ward or administration block (Porta-kabin, really, but 'block' sounds better). No, the real problems began at night when, as the SHO on call, you were 'it'. No other paediatrician remained on site: the consultants were at home, tucked up safely in bed. There were three of us so we worked a one in three rota, but this dropped to one in two – that is, every other day – when an SHO was away on holiday or on sickness leave.

My workload as an SHO was heavy and varied. I was responsible for a paediatric ward always full to capacity with children unwell enough to need admission; children in A&E; acute referrals from GPs; premature babies in their incubators on the Special Care Baby Unit; babies on the postnatal wards; and finally – but busiest of all – labour ward. The digits 6208 appearing on my bleep signified a call from labour ward, demanding my urgent attention.

'Dr Barrie? Are you on for paeds tonight?'

I glanced at my watch. 2.04 a.m. *No, I just happened to be in the hospital at this time and, since I was here, I thought I might as well leave my bleep switched on.*

'Yes,' I sighed.

'Oh good. It's Jacky on labour ward. We've got a primip here, she's fully now but there's mec staining. There was a bit of mec when she was nine centimetres. The trace was showing earlies then but, um, now there's a few lates.'

'OK,' I said to the midwife. 'I'll be straight up.'

At the start of the job I had been muddled by the abundant use of medical jargon. Previously, as a psychiatrist, depression was called depression. Mania was mania. Not so in paediatrics. *Primip* is short for *primipara*, meaning a woman giving birth for the first time. Strictly speaking, *primigravida* (a woman who is pregnant for the first time) is the correct term, and so the midwife should have said 'primig', but there's no such word in the slang vocabulary of doctors and midwives, and the accepted term is 'primip'. By *fully*, Jacky meant that the woman in labour was fully dilated – that is, the cervix has dilated to

94

ten centimetres. *Mec* is meconium, the thick, greenish-black, sticky faeces passed by a baby in the first couple of days of birth. Meconium is also passed by a baby deprived of oxygen within the womb and so is an indication of fetal distress. Jacky was therefore saying that the amniotic fluid, or liquor ('waters'), were stained with meconium.

The labour process is monitored by an electronic trace which detects both the baby's heart beat within the womb and uterine contractions. The baby's pulse is usually steady but invariably it slows as he gets squashed by each contraction. This is known as an *early* deceleration and can easily be seen on the fetal heart trace spewing out of the printer. A distressed infant may, additionally, have slowing of the heart rate extending beyond the duration of the uterine contraction – a *late* deceleration.

I was in A&E when the bleep sounded. I had been asked to see a child who had been unwell for several hours. She was feverish, with a sore throat, and had a faint rash on her chest. Her GP had thought it was probably scarlet fever and quite reasonably had prescribed penicillin. The girl had deteriorated and so her GP had referred her up to see me; I was examining her when Jacky bleeped me. All the tell-tale signs of meningitis were there: a high temperature, a rash that didn't blanch when I pressed it, a stiff neck and an aversion to the light of my pen-torch.

Before Jacky spoke, I knew from the digits on the bleep's display that the call to labour ward would take precedence. It always did. But now what? Before me was a seven-year-old child with probable meningitis and she required a lumbar puncture and intravenous antibiotics. But the woman on labour ward was already fully dilated and would deliver any minute now. It would take four and a half minutes to run to labour ward: I knew the journey time to labour ward from A&E, the ward, the clinic, the postnatal wards and, not that I saw it much, the doctors' mess. For a moment I considered telephoning the on-call consultant but I dismissed the idea. It would take my boss at least twenty minutes to reach the hospital if she was dressed and ready, but in the middle of the night it would take her longer.

'I'll be back in ten minutes,' I said to the girl's parents in a rehearsed apology. Their anxiety was palpable as I hurried off to labour ward. Their daughter was seriously ill but so too was the baby about to be delivered. For one thing, the presence of meconium before birth, together with late decelerations on the trace, indicated fetal distress. Secondly, if meconium had passed into the amniotic fluid – and the midwife, Jacky, said that it had – there was a good chance that some might have entered the baby's mouth. On taking his first breath, the baby might inhale meconium which would result in all manner of respiratory problems. It's vital to reach the labour ward before the infant is born and not a second later.

'Come on! You can do it! Keep it coming, keep it coming, keep pushing.' Jacky was in full swing now, shouting her encouragement at the exhausted mother. The father was by his wife's side, squeezing her hand and staring at the midwife intently, like a small child watching a stranger.

I ran over to the Resuscitair – a glorified work bench with an overhead light and heater. I switched both on, and the two heating bars glowed as the electric current flowed through them. I checked the oxygen supply and the pieces of equipment in the in-built drawer. I'd made sure that I was familiar with all the knobs and buttons on the Resuscitair and now knew it as an old friend. Many a time I had worked on an infant for what seemed like hours, before declaring him or her 'stable' enough to be transferred downstairs to the Special Care Baby Unit.

'Right, she's coming!' Jacky called over to me. I ran forward with a warm, dry towel. '*He*-re she is,' said Jacky as she delivered the baby's head. The baby was covered in vernix caseosum, the greasy chalk-coloured material that coats all newly-born. It was clearly a male infant, although the atmosphere of high tension in the delivery suite precluded an opportunity to laugh at the midwife's earlier assumption.

The baby was what we would call 'flat', meaning he was lifeless. I wrapped him tightly, very tightly in fact, in the towel and, clamping his tiny chest tightly between my hands, stepped five paces back to the Resuscitair. The idea behind chest clamping is to prevent the baby from inhaling meconium before it has been sucked out mechanically, although in this little chap's case I don't think it would have made much difference. I placed him under the bright light. The heater was now hot, which would at least minimise the risk of hypothermia. But he had yet to take his first breath.

Jacky swapped places with me so that she was holding the chest whilst I passed a laryngoscope into the baby's mouth. It was full of evil, green meconium. I quickly inserted a suction tube, first into his mouth and then into both nostrils, pressing the floor pedal so that maximal suction was applied. Blobs of meconium whizzed down the tube and into a canister at the side of the Resuscitair.

He was still not breathing, the reward in preventing meconium aspiration now overshadowed by the starvation of oxygen to his brain. The lips and tongue, clear now of meconium, were tinged blue. I knew that we were running into difficulties.

'Get the consultant!' I shouted, not addressing anyone in particular. No one moved. 'Now!' I saw Jacky motion to one of her assistants. I had the girl waiting in Casualty and could see that I was going to be tied up here for a while yet.

Cautiously I advanced the gleaming silver blade of the laryngoscope towards the back of the baby's throat. Good. No sign of meconium. I angled the blade upwards and at the same time pushed downwards on his tongue.

'Come on, *come on*,' I urged under my breath. I was looking for the vocal cords, when suddenly they sprang into view. The light from the laryngoscope's bulb was bright and I saw its sharp reflection as it bounced off a shiny bead of sticky meconium. I zapped it dry with a blast of suction and the cords, now, were clear.

'Let's intubate,' I said. The baby had not breathed since birth and it was vital that, with the meconium now cleared away, effective respiration commence. If it meant artificially then so be it. I slid a narrow airway into the space between the gaping vocal cords and then withdrew the laryngoscope. I attached a length of tube to the end of the airway sticking out of the mouth and linked it to a rubber ventilator bag. I slowly squeezed the bag, and saw the satisfying rise of baby's chest as the lungs filled with air. The infant turned a healthy, pink colour. After several minutes of hand-ventilation, I disconnected the tube from the airway, and waited; almost instantly he took a deep breath and then coughed the narrow plastic airway outwards. He had passed the test of seeing whether he was able to breathe independently. I carried him over to his mother, who now held him for the first time and I could hear her joyous weeping as I raced down the three flights of stairs back to A&E.

The girl looked terrible. Her thin body was now almost completely covered by a dark, and sinister, purple eruption. She was hot and delirious. Realising the severity of her illness, the nursing staff had contacted the on-call paediatric consultant as soon as I'd hurried off to labour ward but she had not yet arrived. I knew that a lumbar puncture would result in the loss of valuable time and instructed the nurse to administer immediately a high-dose penicillin injection. I set up a drip and pumped more, and stronger, antibiotics into her veins; the futility of aggressive treatment was certain but you have to go on. For the sake of the parents, for the sake of the child, for *my* sake.

By the time the consultant arrived the girl was in a deep coma. I had sat with her parents while the nurses fiddled with her drip set and recorded the oxygen level from the clip on her index finger. Her mother was weeping and her father, cradling his daughter's head in his hands, rocked back and forth, willing that life return to her fading soul.

The baby I'd rushed to earlier was by his mother's side in the postnatal ward. He was pink in colour and each breath seemed to be taken with a purposeful enthusiasm.

He was discharged after a few days and his parents gave me an over-sized card. A big thank-you for everything you did, they'd written. I kept it in the doctors' clinic office and they would remark on it when they returned for their child's routine follow-up visits.

As the months passed it became clear that all was not well. At eight months, Callum was developing abnormal involuntary movements and was not yet sitting unsupported – the characteristic 'tripod' position normally seen by six months of age. His brain had been starved of oxygen for too long around the time of his birth, and I spent some time explaining the correlation between his birth asphyxia and his emerging cerebral palsy.

Just as I was about to leave one evening, after a tiring day which had followed a night on call, the brightly painted bear on their card caught my eye. I'd been in the hospital two full days and hadn't had any sleep whatsoever. The bear winked outwardly, supposedly at the card's recipient, with a silvery italicised 'thank you' printed beneath his waving paw. I thought back to the night when Callum had been born; to Jacky's telephone call; and to my subsequent actions. What did I do that was good? What quality of life had I endowed on this hapless child? And what about the seven-year-old who had died in order for Callum to live? Might she have survived if I had ignored the summons to labour ward? Might she have lived and Callum *never* lived? A better solution for all, perhaps?

What am I saying? Hospitals are made of bricks and mortar, and they absorb the spirits of the suffering patients and their hopeful beloved who come to breathe the life-giving air encompassed by its walls. The atmosphere is always compassionate and not always healing, and surely only the most insensitive would deny its existence. So who, therefore, am I to pass comment on Callum's quality of life? That goes for his parents, too. Only Callum himself, in years to come, could answer that question.

I tore the card up into many pieces. It was light as I made my way across the extensive car park that flanks three sides of the hospital building. I was so angry.

Roopal awaited my return and, in the evening at our Surbiton flat, she listened whilst I agonised over my future career path. Until then I had wavered between paediatrics and general practice. The choice between being an all-round doctor for children or an all-round doctor for everyone. I talked, she soothed.

The next day was my last as a paediatric SHO. My mind had been made up.

8

My father's brother Julian, a retired ear, nose and throat surgeon, lives in Swansea on the Welsh coast. We would, from time to time, stay with him and his ever-welcoming wife. One autumn half-term, on such a visit to his home on the Gower Peninsula, my father, sister and I were walking with Uncle Julian along the cliff path that runs from the bottom of his garden to the beach at Langland Bay. It's an idyllic spot.

'Can't tell you why it's called Gower,' said Julian, puffing as the gradient of the path underfoot steepened. 'The only Gower I know,' he continued, 'is David Gower, our famous left-handed cricketer.'

'Or there's the Gower who qualified at our alma mater,' my father said.

'You mean UCH?' Julian shot a quizzical look at my father. My father and Julian had both qualified from University College Hospital, London, and prior to that had attended the same grammar school: the term *alma mater* was therefore ambiguous.

'Yes, University College,' my father said. 'But back in

the 1860s. And whilst there he was a protégé of Sir William Jenner, whom he greatly admired. His area of expertise was neurology and he was one of its most able practitioners.'

'I have one of his books in my consulting room,' Julian interrupted. 'Picked it up at a second-hand book shop in Cardiff. What's it called now? Oh yes: *Diagnosis of Diseases of the Spinal Cord*.'

'Well then,' continued my father. 'He also wrote *A Manual of the Diseases of the Nervous System*', which ran to two volumes and which he illustrated himself. Did you know that his paintings were so good that they were exhibited at the Royal Academy? He was a very precise man and great proponent of shorthand.'

'Mind the rocks to your left,' said Julian as we neared Mumbles Head. 'Yes Herbert, I knew about the short-hand, in fact I think I read about it in one of the UCH newsletters a few years back. It's said that he once grabbed a complete stranger in the street and said "Young man, do you write shorthand?" The stranger, reeling from surprise, replied "No sir, I do not." Gower dropped the man's arm in disgust and retorted "You are a fool and will fail in life!"'

Julian and his brother continued to discuss Gower in the context of their old medical school.

'Sounds quite a character,' I said lamely.

'Sure!' my father continued. 'He wasn't just an expert in shorthand. Oh no! He studied wild flowers, mosses, architecture, archaeology and Suffolk churches. He classified nervous diseases. And most importantly—'

'He described the famous sign of muscular dystrophy,' finished Julian.

I hadn't understood this last bit of the biographical resumé on Gower but the conversation between the two brothers drifted off to some or other subject and I soon forgot all about it.

Billy had had an uneventful early childhood. His birth had been unremarkable: born at term, normal delivery, no problems. He had developed normally and attained his milestones at appropriate ages. Early gross motor skills such as rolling over, sitting, and standing, had been mastered without difficulty, and he had taken his first steps at twelve months.

Now his mother looked worried.

She had brought Billy to the surgery because she had noticed a gradual, though steady, decline in his strength and he appeared to be falling with increasing frequency. I hadn't encountered such a problem before but could tell that he was going to present something of a diagnostic enigma. I pulled the toy box from under the couch and let Billy occupy himself with its contents while his mother provided me with more details.

I'd been taught that there's far more to be learnt by watching a child play than from examining him, when all but the most confident of children will freeze up and refuse to cooperate. Indeed, the most accurate assessment of a child's health and development can be made this way, and with this in mind I kept my eyes trained on Billy whilst his mother told me that he 'had not been right' for eight months. His legs had weakened, she said, and he tended to stumble. He needed assistance to stand and once upright his stance was peculiar: awkward, with his belly sticking out in front.

She went on to tell me that although she'd suspected for some weeks that something wasn't right, it wasn't until Billy had started at nursery that she saw how far he was behind the other children. It was this which had prompted today's visit.

I observed Billy as we spoke and saw a happy four-year-old lad with normal fine motor skills, dexterity and coordination. He sneezed suddenly and a large blob of mucus shot from one nostril onto his sweater. His mother cast an apologetic look toward me and, fishing a large paper tissue from out of her coat pocket, called him over. It was then that I witnessed something which previously I had only read about.

Billy manoeuvred his body so that he was perched on all fours with both knees straightened, and he then began to literally 'climb' up his legs with his hands gripped alternately around each thigh. At once I thought of Swansea and dear Uncle Julian and our walk along the cliff to Mumbles. So this was Gower's sign! It's in all the books but I was seeing it now first hand; and once seen, never forgotten.

Gower's sign is suggestive, indeed probably diagnostic, of muscular dystrophy. I quickly checked for other classic signs of this condition and they too were present. The muscular dystrophies are a group of unrelated diseases, each with a differing genetic cause and clinical present-ation. I referred Billy to the paediatricians, who confirmed the diagnosis and specified the exact type of muscular dystrophy that Billy had.

I saw much of him, and his anxiety-stricken mother, in the weeks that followed his diagnosis. She wished answers to numerous questions, and wanted honesty from me. She felt that the hospital doctors were being over-optimistic, enthusiastic even, and I attempted to bridge the gap between Billy and his specialist. I did not want to cast doom and gloom on an already fraught clinical situation, but equally if she came away from our endless discussions believing that the worst was over then they would have failed in their purpose.

Billy became confined to his wheelchair at the age of eleven, and died four years later from the inevitable respiratory complications of his illness.

He never saw the beautiful coastline of the Gower Peninsula.

9

My first job in general practice was in Great Bookham, a misnomer as it is a small village, and being out in the sticks in leafy Surrey there's not much great about it. It's a nice enough place, though, and I was fortunate to work for a friendly doctor, Graham Chinn, who was eager to teach me the essential skills of family doctoring. We got on very well. By happy coincidence, the parents of a good school chum, later to be my best man and later still to purchase a house on the old West Park Hospital site, lived in the village. On discovering I had been posted to their local surgery, they insisted that I stay with them; and so 1994 proved to be a happy and pleasurable introduction to my chosen career.

The time came soon enough, however, to find a practice of my own and each Saturday morning I would pore over the classified section of the *British Medical Journal*, seeking suitable partnership vacancies. The first such post to attract my attention was in Tadworth, another out-in-the-sticks Surrey backwater. I was invited for an interview and soon after was informed that I'd successfully passed to the next stage of the appointment process.

'I don't understand,' I said, and then rather precisely, 'Does that mean I've got the job?'

'Not exactly,' explained the senior partner at Tadworth. 'You are invited, along with your wife naturally, for drinks tomorrow. Shall we say eight o'clock?'

'Ah! The infamous trial by sherry!' Graham Chinn later exclaimed. 'I thought that went out with the Ark. Even I didn't have to go through that all those hundreds of years ago. Good luck, old chum.'

And so it was that the next day Roopal and I drove over the Epsom Downs to Tadworth, where a welcoming party awaited us: the five Tadworth doctors with their assorted spouses. For an hour we held court, if not our own, and at ten o'clock they told us to leave.

The following Saturday Roopal made sure she was first to open the *British Medical Journal*. Tadworth had demurred on the telephone a few days after my trial by sherry, and when Roopal saw the advertisement for a partnership vacancy in Kingston upon Thames, the town of both our childhoods, we both knew that it might just be what fate had kept in store for me. I applied, took a look around the practice, and a couple of weeks later was shortlisted.

The interview was a relaxed and laid-back affair. The youngest partner was leaving for family reasons, and the remaining two doctors were easy-going and very convivial.

'Any questions you might like to ask *us*?' asked Dr David Jebb, one of the general practitioners and a practice partner.

I paused before asking, 'Um, do you … I mean, do I need to have a glass of sherry with you?' What the hell, I thought. I needed to know if I had to endure another damned sherry trial.

David Jebb chortled loudly. 'Why, goodness no! Can't stand the stuff. We can have a coffee now if you want, but I'd far sooner get away home,' he said.

He and Dr Maria Strzelecka, the senior of the two partners, shook my hand warmly and asked me when I could start.

And so it was that in August 1995 I joined the three-doctor partnership at the Richmond Road Medical Centre. The surgery is housed in a Victorian building which was actually built as a doctor's residence-cum-practice. When its doors opened to patients, one century earlier in 1895, the 'clinical' area of the house was limited to just two rooms on the ground floor. An inter-connecting door linked these two rooms, and both had separate doors to the hall of the house. One, the waiting room, also opened directly onto the front garden and presumably the patients would enter the waiting room through this door, and then be called by the doctor – resplendent in tails, watch and a chain adorning his waistcoat – who at the end of morning surgery would retreat for coffee through his own door leading to the rest of the house. Here four reception rooms on the ground floor were for his family's personal use, and likewise several more rooms on the first floor. To complete the Victorian grandeur there was (and still is) a large basement and attic for staff quarters.

The list size grew and by the 1950s there were two, then three, doctors practising at the surgery, with the doctor-owner having to relinquish the entire ground floor for patients' use. The house was impractical now for his expanding family and their servants to entirely occupy the first and second floors, with the butler and chauffeur stuck in the basement two floors below. He therefore converted the basement, first and top floor into flats and to this day I meet patients who tell me that they have lived in one of the bedsits.

The massive building projects undertaken in Kingston in the mid to late nineties resulted in a huge boost to the borough's population. The new home owners were well off and young, with their babies arriving soon after. The patient list grew until there came a point when the practice simply could not accommodate the flux of ill people. Gone today are the bedsits and the quaint interconnecting door. Gone, too, is the door leading onto the street. Patients use the main entrance – indeed, it is their ingress into what has become their entire building.

The front garden has been paved, thereby creating the ubiquitous off-street car park. On a busy morning today there might be the cars of four doctors, two nurses, a counsellor, the midwife and a health visitor. The team of managers, social worker, psychologist and dietitian complete the multi-disciplinary squad.

I remember a young lad who came to see me a few months after I had started at Richmond Road. He had just turned thirteen and, in anxious self-assessment of his pubertal progress, had discovered that one testis felt different from the other. Oliver was shy and embarrassed, but allowed me to examine him while he and his mother nervously awaited the diagnosis. To their consternation, I couldn't make one. It was evident that his left testis was enlarged, hinting at a testicular tumour, but I could not confidently say what type of tumour. This is normal: it's virtually impossible to identify tumour type on clinical examination. But without a diagnosis, of course, one cannot predict the disease's natural history or, more bluntly, its outlook.

It was clear that a referral was needed, but to whom? I felt a certain antipathy toward the general surgeons at Kingston after the junior job I'd endured under their jurisdiction. There is an excellent urologist at Kingston but he was on annual leave so it had to be elsewhere. Medics say 'St Elsewhere' when referring to anywhere other than the hospital immediately to hand, and so to St Elsewhere it had to be. I thought hard for a moment.

'So,' I summed up, 'it'll have to be London. St Thomas's in London. That OK?'

Oliver's mother was ambivalent.

'And I know just the man,' I continued. 'His name is Mr Finch.'

Eric Finch was a general surgeon and not a urologist, but he was no ordinary general surgeon: he was a *master* surgeon of extreme proficiency and skill. Moreover, I had once witnessed him remove a testicular tumour on a lad not much older than Oliver, and the memory of the operation had remained with me since.

The patient was a Pakistani boy who, like Oliver, had found a lump in his scrotum. Finch decided that the entire testis, not just the tumour, had to be removed and the boy was listed for surgery that afternoon. The house officer scribbled a few notes, completed a consent form, which he asked the boy's father to sign, administered a pre-med and then hurried down to the theatre to change into his greens. I, and the other medical students on the firm, were already in the operating room; we knew Finch's pre-dilection for punctuality and made sure we'd arrived early. We stood idly and awkwardly in our green pyjamas with a disposable mask tied around our necks and a paper cap on our heads. Finch strode in at 2 o'clock sharp, and at once silence descended on the assembled crowd. The theatre technicians, the scrub nurse, my group of students, even the consultant anaesthetist, sensed the commanding presence of the great man. Nobody stirred, not even so much as twitched, as he gave each of us a brief glare – his stern eyes famously unyielding. There was, it had to be said, a certain elegance about his superiority which was contrasted, drastically, by the crashing entrance of his house officer, Terry Wilkins.

'You're late,' scowled Finch.

'I'm sorry but I was getting the first patient ready for theatre,' began Wilkins. 'I had to complete the paperwork.'

But Finch wasn't listening, or at least gave no indication that he had registered that Dr Wilkins had even spoken.

Wilkins hurried over to the large stainless steel basin and scrubbed up alongside his boss. Both men took up their places facing each other across the narrow operating table. The Pakistani boy lay anaesthetised and unconscious and helpless as Finch cleaned his skin with a thick, gooey solution handed to him by the scrub nurse. He held the sponge forceps delicately, much like an artist holding a paintbrush.

'Left side, Wilkins. Right?'

'Right, sir,' said Wilkins.

'What, right as in the other side or correct?' Finch's tone was impatient.

'Sorry, I mean correct.' Wilkins blushed.

'Fool,' I heard Finch mutter under his breath.

Finch made a large incision over the left side of the scrotum and then looked up at the seven of us jostling for space behind Wilkins. A look of fear flashed across the house officer's face, then relief as he realised that we and not himself were the target of his boss's glare. Finch scanned the row of heads and settled his stare on Nabhi Shah.

'If you care to look properly, you will see the spermatic cord arising from the left testis,' said Finch, clamping the cord with a pair of shiny Spencer Wells forceps. 'Here!' he added triumphantly, looking up once more at Nabhi. 'I want to know what it contains.'

Nabhi then reeled off the anatomical contents of the spermatic cord while Finch continued with the operation. He worked quickly but methodically, and the scrub nurse by his side ensured that she anticipated correctly each of his commands for an instrument to be passed.

I cannot remember the exact sequence of events which followed because it all happened so fast. I can remember Finch unclamping the spermatic cord and, lifting the Spencer Wells clamp high in his right hand, hurling it just above Nabhi's head. It hit the clock on the opposite wall and the glass casing shattered. Nabhi had ducked just in time and Wilkins sniggered. Finch then backed away from the operating table and began to make his way towards the opposite side where Nabhi was standing, rooted to the spot between me and Philomena Taumer. Wilkins, assuming that his body presented an obstacle in Finch's path to reach his desired victim, stood to one side. But Finch's direction now altered, and he was up against Wilkins at the head of the table. And throughout these perplexing few seconds there was complete silence.

Finch turned momentarily to Nabhi.

'Thank you, Shah. Very good,' he smiled. Then he turned back to Wilkins, but his expression had once again turned cold. Now he glared at the bewildered young doctor standing before him.

'Give me another name for testis.'

'Sorry?' said Wilkins.

'You heard me.'

'Oh right, sir, er...'

'Why do you keep saying right when you mean *correct*? Or are you stalling for time?' inquired Finch. 'I want another name.'

'*Testicles*,' said Wilkins, stretching the word out so long that one of the nurses stifled a giggle.

'NO!' roared Finch. 'Another! Gimme another!'

Wilkins was red-faced now from embarrassment.

'*Orch*-ids,' he said. 'Um, orchids.'

'If I wanted a sodding flower,' screamed Finch, 'I would have asked for one.' He moved his face even closer to Wilkins, who trembled in front of his boss's steely glare. He looked around the operating theatre and, as one, we at once studied our feet.

'B-a-l-l-s,' Wilkins said uncertainly, his voice now quavering.

'Ah,' said Finch. '*Now* you're getting warm. Come on, keep going. Nearly there.'

Wilkins cast his eyes around the theatre. The instrument tray glistened beside the scrub nurse, who now fiddled with a stitch holder.

'Bollocks,' said Wilkins hesitantly.

'Louder!' Finch yelled. 'Louder!'

'Bollocks,' repeated Wilkins although not much greater in amplification.

'Yes! Bollocks! And that just about sums up your feeble bollock-sized, bollock-consistency, bollockable brain. You, oh-so-stupid-one, have consented this boy for a *left* orchidectomy. But there's nothing wrong with his left testis; the tumour is on the *right*. If I'd removed his good testis then this lad would be dead in four months. You know why? Because the cancerous testis would've been left behind, that's why. Luckily for you, twit, I inspected *both* testes before cutting the left spermatic cord and removing the testis dangling beneath it.'

The memory of the humiliation of the hapless young doctor in front of students junior to him, and in front of the anaesthetist and nurses too, has stayed with me. But it taught me to check which side of the body I am referring to in written notes, especially those penned to colleagues. I always check that I am injecting, or operating on, or describing, the right – *correct* – side.

And Oliver? I knew that he was in safe hands.

10

April 2002 and I attended a meeting at Charing Cross Hospital. Walking through the unadorned and faceless grey anonymous entrance hall of the largest building in Fulham, I couldn't help but feel sad: my father had worked here as consultant paediatrician from the sixties until the early eighties. He was respected and much liked by his colleagues and staff; he ran a renowned department which accepted referrals from not just the local community but also from other hospitals afar. It was here that he built his Special Care Baby Unit (SCBU) – a 'baby' in its own right of his own making – and this became a hot bed of innovation and expertise.

And here, too, was where my mother had practised as a consultant microbiologist. Energetic, intelligent and popular, she was nothing other than a first-class doctor and first-class mother.

My father, Herbert, saw the need to further the success already borne out by his unit, and others like it, and with the help of funds raised by the grateful parents of premature babies saved by the SCBU, he built a paediatric research laboratory. The hospital trustees gave him a small patch of land in the front of the hospital – near to its junction with St Dunstan's Road – on which to construct this project, and he was proud of the laboratory, which in time employed a full-time technician and carried out cutting-edge research into neonatal respiratory physiology and intensive care.

Increasing numbers of premature babies were surviving against all odds and often we would open the Sunday papers to see another feature on my father's SCBU at Charing Cross. He lived and breathed this aspect of his work: paediatric outpatients and ward rounds had, he said, an inescapable monotony, but neonatal special care? Ah, he would sigh, *that* was different. I liked to accompany him on a Saturday or Sunday morning to the SCBU and I would watch as he checked every baby, examining each tiny infant carefully, after which he would discuss the baby's progress with the parents and his team.

I would, on occasion, help him put up a mirror in the nurses' office; or lay a new lino on the floor of the parents' suite; or assemble an item of cheap furniture. My father recoiled from managers and administrators, whom he found at best unhelpful and at worst obstructive. Why hassle yourself asking for a job to be done when you know they'll find any excuse to say No? he would say. If his juniors complained that extra shelves were needed to house babies' medical notes, then he would bring in his saw and some wood and a masonry drill, and put the shelves up himself.

Once, on a family holiday in Rome, I remember my father being besotted by a porcelain tondo hanging in the hotel bedroom. It was of the Virgin mother and child, and he was adamant that something like this should adorn the wall above the bank of incubators in his SCBU back in London. It was important, he said, for the mothers to know that love was very much a part of the ethos of the Unit, and for the junior doctors not to lose sight of humanity, which should be inherent in their work. Each baby is a little human being, with a heart and a soul, my father said, and not a bundle of tissue-papered skin and bone and tubes much as journalists were wont to think.

The hotel manager was not, much to my father's utter dismay, prepared to sell the tondo and so the family embarked on a search of the city for a pottery where one might be able to purchase such a thing. We struck lucky on the third day and came back from Rome with not one, but two, beautiful glazed tondos – one being a spare in case of breakage!

I thought back to this happy day as I negotiated my way through the now-unfamiliar hospital to the room where the meeting was scheduled to take place. I've never worked at Charing Cross Hospital; my only knowledge of the dreary labyrinth made up by its corridors is from my visits as a child when I'd accompanied my father and the unforgettable day when the hospital was the venue for my clinical 'finals'.

But by April 2002 much had changed. The NHS 're-organisation' of the 1980s had forced the paediatric department at Charing Cross to merge with its sister unit at Westminster Hospital. At about the same time a state-of-the-art hospital was being built in Chelsea, and it was here that my father's department moved soon after he'd retired.

The twenty years my father had spent propagating his illustrious department counted, in the end, for nothing – at least, that's how it seems to me. But the clinical advances made within his Paediatric Research Laboratory were published and, arguably, have left an indelible mark on paediatric practice the world over.

Neonatal resuscitation and intensive care methods have been adapted and shaped and improved because of them. But like a family home, the bricks and mortar count for as much (maybe more?) than the human characteristics and traits within. The substance of the home is comforting by virtue of its permanence, just as continuance of the occupiers' personalities is hopefully ensured by genetic inheritance.

Memories can be bittersweet. After the meeting had finished on that April day, I walked to where the paediatric department had once stood. The door to my father's office now had a name-plate which read 'LIAISON FACILITATIONS MANAGER'. I haven't a clue what this means. The door was closed and I was thankful for this: at least I couldn't see into the room. My father was for ever being sent photographs of children who had 'emerged' alive from the SCBU and he would display the images of these survivors with immense pride. I remember on one wall there was a huge photograph of a girl called Sarah who had survived despite severe prematurity and next to this my father had displayed a graph charting her early growth in height. Pushed into the glass, in one corner, he had put a photograph of Sarah on the day of her engagement.

The research laboratory has now gone and in its place is a 'pay and display' car park accessed by a new entrance from St Dunstan's Road. A little further on I found where the SCBU once was. This too has gone, and the area has been knocked about to provide a suite of managerial offices. I stood still and tried to imagine the large nursery with its incubators, blood gas machines and bleeping monitors, and for an instant I could picture the hustle and bustle of the Unit, with my father auscultating the tiny chest of a twenty-nine-weeker at the far end of the room. Then the image was gone and I was back in the still quiet of the air-conditioned office suite.

As I turned to go, I glanced up at the walls around me. They were white and plain, not a picture in sight. The tondo had gone. I know not where.

11

Susannah's early life had been punctuated by frequent attendances at the surgery. She seemed to be easily infected by coughs and colds, and was one of those kids who continually had catarrh or a bad chest. Her mother despaired at the amount of antibiotics she'd received over a comparatively short space of time and her doctor, baffled by his apparent inability to formulate a convincing diagnosis which might explain her ill health, arranged a paediatric opinion. The specialist was adamant: Susannah had asthma. She would improve, he reassured, with appropriate treatment.

The GP – my predecessor – duly prescribed anti-asthma inhalers at the behest of the paediatric consultant, but from the comments with which he annotated the specialist's letters it was evident that he was unimpressed with the validity of the diagnosis.

By the time I arrived at the practice in August 1995, Susannah had been attending the paediatric outpatient clinic for six years. Her medical file today bulges with correspondence from the hospital doctors; some advising dosage alterations, others that some new-fangled inhaler or other should be prescribed. And yet, despite all this, Susannah didn't get any better. By her tenth birthday she had missed many weeks from school and when she was brought to the surgery it was invariably 'For her chest, doctor'; I would chat to mother, listen to the lungs, prescribe an antibiotic and, Yes, I would say, stay off school until better.

In the normal course of events I would refer a case such as this to the hospital clinic, where appropriate investigations would, I hope, be set in train. But Susannah was already under the auspices of the paediatric consultant. So what now?

I thought very carefully about the routes open to me: doing nothing wasn't an option; talking the case through with her paediatrician would, I felt, have gained little. They too could see that she coughed her way through winter and autumn, and even the summer months weren't without their share of upper respiratory symptoms. No, this too wasn't an option.

I decided to refer Susannah to the adult respiratory team. I spoke to Susannah, and both she and her mother were in agreement. I discussed the case with Geoff Knowles, the chest physician whose house job I had done immediately after qualifying as a doctor. He promised he'd call me once he had seen Susannah in his clinic. He kept to his word.

'Got any patients with CF?' he said.

'CF?' I repeated. 'You mean cystic fibrosis? None at present. Surely you don't mean that Susannah...?' My words drifted away as the reality of our conversation hit home. Cystic fibrosis is a congenital condition where the various glands of the body produce thick, sticky mucinous secretions which clog up the ducts and passages into which they normally discharge. The disease affects boys and girls equally and presents in early childhood with repeated lower respiratory tract infections caused by the obstruction of bronchi by viscid secretions within the lungs. Indeed, the other name for cystic fibrosis is 'mucoviscidosis'.

One in twenty or so are carriers of the CF gene, and such a person might or might not pass the gene to his offspring; it's a 50:50 chance, like flipping a coin. But if a carrier meets another carrier then the potential for disaster is far greater; for if this couple were, say, to have four children then, statistically speaking, one child would have the full-blown disease, two would be carriers and one would be 'normal'. Carriers are disease-free and therefore well, and Susannah's parents would have had no inkling that they were in silent possession of a gene that was causing their daughter to suffer.

Having proved that Susannah had cystic fibrosis, Geoff Knowles clearly had something of an unforetold dilemma on his hands.

'You see,' he continued. 'I don't want to upset my paediatric colleagues but I think it's fair to say that they missed the diagnosis. Maybe it was easier, or just less difficult, for me.'

'What do you mean?' I asked.

'Well, the paediatricians had been seeing Susannah for so many years that they probably couldn't see the wood for the trees.' Knowles paused, adding with a hint of amusement in his voice, 'Or the trachea for the alveoli.'

'Yes,' I agreed.

'I was able to stand back and look at this case afresh. I read your referral letter, Michael, but I purposely didn't wade through all her old hospital notes.'

Knowles went on to say that he would like the paediatricians to 'have her back' for another year or so as he reckoned they were better equipped to deal with the needs of a fifteen-year-old.

'The clinical part is straightforward,' said Knowles. 'But the paediatric clinic has direct access to an educational psychologist and a paediatric dietitian and social workers – you know the kind of thing I mean.'

Indeed I did. I also knew what he was getting at. Cystic

fibrosis teenagers are renowned for having an awkward and surly temperament. Careful handling and plentiful encouragement is important but is not usually sufficient. It's as well to involve psychologists, school liaison officers, the school nurse and the paediatric outreach team from early on.

'I'll have a chat with the paediatricians this afternoon and explain my involvement. I'll say that you asked me to give an opinion, that's all.'

'Be diplomatic!' I urged.

'What? Yes, I will. Oh and don't forget,' Knowles said, before putting down the telephone, 'send her back to me when she's outgrown the paediatricians.'

No one likes to be chided by a colleague, no matter how politely it's done.

'But why did you refer Susannah to the respiratory physician? Geoff's an adults' doctor. He sees *adult* patients. You should've sent her back to us.' The paediatrician wasn't shouting but he spoke concisely and abruptly and with conviction. I listened whilst I was berated for my actions.

'Never mind all that,' I replied lamely. 'Dr Knowles has made the diagnosis, hasn't he? Isn't that what matters?'

'We could have made it too. I dare say we would've when we saw her again in the clinic.'

'Perhaps,' I lied. 'She's due to be seen for the umpteenth time by the umpteenth junior member of your team. Anyway, must go. I've pressing things to attend to.' I gently replaced the receiver: the crash-bang of hanging-up is a 'stage effect' which serves only to inflame and infuriate.

Susannah's passage along the path to an improved state of health was far from smooth. Yet she was a determined young girl with a steely will to get both better and fitter.

She never let on to her friends the true severity of her condition and she completed her education with admirable resolution.

She looks after her illness pretty much herself these days and has an amazing insight into CF and the drugs that sustain her. So much so, in fact, that I rarely see her in the surgery. She popped in a few weeks back with a favour to ask. Would I mind, she asked, counter-signing her application form for a new-style driver's licence card?

'Sure!' I said. 'I'd be delighted.' I signed the form and photograph, and handed them back to her. She thanked me and then turned to leave.

'Wait a minute!' I called out. Susannah hesitated at the door and glanced back expectantly. 'That means you're seventeen,' I said. 'I think it's about time you stopped seeing the kiddies' doctor at the hospital. I know a nice chest physician; can I make the arrangements?'

Susannah flashed a warm, approving smile and was gone.

12

The future of a hospital lies in the men who work
in its halls and in the ideals which they cherish and teach.

William Osler
1849–1919

We called her Madam Chop Chop. Early thirties, almost
certainly privately educated, just as certainly London-
trained. Why the latter, you ask? Graduates from London
medical establishments adopt a rather superficial air of
superiority; a kind of superciliousness not seen amongst
those who have trained at a provincial medical school.
When I was a student, indeed in the days when Madam
Chop Chop strutted along the central corridor of St
Thomas's Hospital, there existed a healthy clutch of
London schools: St Thomas's (seemingly I too am guilty
of this aforementioned snobbery by placing it first!),
Guy's, the London (in Whitechapel and so, it might be
said, undeserving of its presupposed elitism), St George's,
St Bartholomew's (known to all as 'Bart's'), Charing Cross

and Westminster, King's College, St Mary's, University College (where my father, my uncle and his son, David, trained), the Middlesex and the Royal Free.

Each was justly proud of its history and rich culture. Each boasted renowned alumni – from St Thomas's hailed Keats, W. Somerset Maugham, Lord (David) Owen (of SDP fame) and Brian Creamer. And each enjoyed lasting anecdotes which, by virtue of their being passed from generation to generation, became notable and, in time, celebrated. At Tommies we had the student who decades if not *centuries* earlier had chopped the penis off 'his' cadaver and then brandished it at some unsuspecting fellow Tube passengers.

There is the one about a student, a rib and a mighty pissed-off anatomy examiner. We were expected to know all there is to know about every bone in the body, which obviously includes being able to identify it. The ribs were no exception. The knack, as always, was in the *delivery*.

'Ah yes, let me see. Well, I can make out the insertion of the intercostals ... and here [*pointing*] is the groove for the neurovascular bundle. Mmm, I can see the notch made by the internal mammary artery. So ... er ... mmm, must be the, um [*looking up, earnest expression, wide-eyed – don't blink if you're male, two blinks if female, three if pretty female student and male examiner/good-looking male student and female examiner/camp examiner* (although I have yet to meet a camp anatomist)] ... right ... um ... s e v e n t h rib.'

Where was I? Oh yes, so there's this nervous student and a crusty bespectacled examiner. The examiner leads the candidate over to a table of bones and invites him to pick one out. Any one, he says. Those who have gone before always advise that you *avoid the subject about which you know everything.* Fatal mistake, they warn. Nothing worse than the year geek, the omnipotent smart-arse, the proverbial bloody know-it-all. The examiner will enjoy tying you up in knots on the minutiae of your blessed specimen/bone/X-ray/electrocardiogram.

It's funny how examination technique can be so crucial and so deciding. I once failed a *viva voce* examination because, in response to a question about oesophageal varices, I said that there were ten ways to stem the bleeding. Great! said the examiner, let's hear them. He held up both hands in the air, fingers outstretched straight, and proceeded to bend each one over as I stumbled my way through the blasted list. Unfortunately, a mixture of nerves and panic precluded me from remembering the last one.

Forgotten the last, have we? sneered the examiner. He held up his single remaining digit and waved it at me. The next student, Mr Wise Guy, was asked the same question. Ah, he began, there are several methods to halt the bleeding varices … and he went on to list eight – bloody hell, *eight* – such methods. He passed while I failed by drawing attention to the 'missing' one.

Anyway, where was I again? Oh yeah – the poor chap looks at the array of bones on the table. They're set out neatly, as they always are in examinations, and the student lingers for a while, uncertain which one to choose.

'Go on,' says the aged anatomist. 'If you take much longer, you'll probably end up a pile of bones yourself. A centre of ossification *par excellence*.'

The student feigns a weak, polite smile and with sudden decisiveness picks up a small rib. It is quite obvious that he hasn't held one before. He grabs it with both hands, one at each end as one might a spare rib at the Wild West Cowboy Restaurant. Then realising his error, he quickly lets go of one end and holds the rib aloft with his right hand. But he has chosen a small rib and its curve gives the impression that it's about to be flung as a miniature boomerang.

'Ah, I see you've picked a rib,' exclaims the anatomist with alacrity, emphasising the name of the bone in anticipation of *schadenfreude*. The medical student's face falls in disappointment at the lost opportunity to identify the object, for he had hoped to win favour with the examiner by pondering the bone for a while and then venturing that It Might, Sir, Just Happen To Be A Rib.

'Well now,' continues the old man, 'so we have here a rib. I thought it might be fun [*fun?*] to talk a little about the embryology of the aforesaid rib. You know,' he says smiling with insincere benevolence, 'how it, um, came to be. The science of the Garden of the Eden, if you've ever read that story.'

'You mean Adam...' interrupts the student, but the examiner isn't listening.

'Yes,' continues the learned professor, 'we can talk about which cell lines formed this rib, and you can tell me all about endoderm, mesoderm and ectoderm. As I'm sure you know, only one of these is pertinent to the formation of bone. But more of that later. Now I want you to tell me what rib this is.'

'Is? You mean, what it is?'

'Please.'

'I'm sorry, sir. I don't understand.'

'Where it's from, young man,' says the old man in exasperation. *Give me strength*, he thought. *Any fool knows that this has to be the twelfth rib, right side, of course.*

There are twelve pairs of ribs and the eleventh and twelfth pair, at the lower end of the chest, are small and rudimentary. The examiner, with increasing impatience, would be happy with eleventh or twelfth.

The student turns the rib over, again and again, not for one moment taking his eyes off the bone. He curses himself for having chosen the damn thing. Oh bloody hell!

And then it suddenly dawns on him.

'A rabbit, sir.'

'I beg your pardon?' says the examiner.

'A rabbit,' repeats the student with a smile.

'What are you talking about?'

'The bone. I mean the rib. It's from a rabbit, sir.'

'What on earth are you saying?'

The student's face falls in despair. *A rib. Why a rib? Why didn't I choose a femur, or a radius? I don't know where this bloody thing is from. Looks pretty small to me. Guess could be from a child – no, unlikely, the medical school wouldn't be able to get their hands on the body. Shit! Shit! Shit!*

He really thought he had cracked it. Obviously not.

'Must be a dog or a cat,' he said.

'What? Do you –'

'Maybe a hare?'

'No! No! Stop it at once,' screeches the old professor, the veins on his temples beginning to swell.

'Oh I've got it!' ventures the student. 'A possum! That's it! A possum.'

The letter from the Dean arrived at the hapless student's hall of residence a few days later. The Dean chided him for his ignorance and wrote: 'If you had intended to be an animals' doctor then you should have gone to veterinary school'. He concluded his letter with the words: 'Your insistence in persevering with stupid answers is an impudence that this medical school will not tolerate.'

Anyway, what's all this got to do with Madam Chop Chop? Rather a lot, actually. Like the venerable anatomy professor, she was equally impatient. But he was old and time-worn, she a junior obstetric registrar, which made her intolerance seem churlish. Her utterance at every conceivable opportunity of the echoing 'chop chop' had quickly earned her her nickname.

One day, on a ward round in the maternity department, she fires a question at one of the firm.

'What are the two principal causes of an antepartum haemorrhage?' she asks, looking at the entourage assembled at the end of the patient's bed. 'Yes Katie, your turn.'

Katie hesitates for just a second.

'Chop chop! I haven't got all day,' barks Chop Chop.

'*Placenta praevia* and, er...' Katie's calm response is rudely interrupted.

'Yes? Come on! Chop chop! *Placenta praevia* and *abruptio placentae*. Right? Good. Er, Nabhi, tell me about abruption. Quickly! Chop chop!'

In theatres she was worse. Everything and everyone had to be waiting, ready and prepared for the arrival of Madam Chop Chop. Woe betide the poor nurse who faltered, even momentarily, when asked to pass an instrument.

'Hagar. Size ten Hagar. Now!'

The scrub nurse rummages on her tray and picks out a size ten Hagar cervical dilator.

'Chop chop!' yells Chop Chop. And so it went on.

But all these are tales of old. Past tense, dear reader. I've already said that St Thomas's Hospital Medical School no longer exists. And neither does Charing Cross, nor Mary's, nor indeed most of the London medical schools. They have been swallowed up by unruly mergers and amalgamations to create equally unruly and bigger, though not better, establishments with meaningless names such as Imperial College and 'GKT' – the letters which denote the messy coalescence of Guy's, King's and beloved St Thomas's.

The handsome medical school building of the latter, opposite the Houses of Parliament and adjacent to

Archbishop's Palace, occupies a precious riverside site in the heart of the capital. In 1998 it was acquired by King's College and the building is now disused. In a controversial bid, the Aga Khan has offered £24 million to develop the site as an Islamic cultural centre. And why not? If the spiritual leader of twenty million Ismaili Muslims wants to build the largest Islamic museum and cultural centre in the English-speaking world, then he should be applauded. The medical school building undoubtedly holds countless memories for me but my true affection is reserved for the institution, now long gone, not bricks and mortar.

There has never been a more important time to honour and understand Islam. When the Council of King's College examines the Aga Khan's proposal, it would do well to distance itself from those urging protection of the site recently vacated by St Thomas's Hospital Medical School. The Council members have been sent a letter, co-signed by Virginia Bottomley (the one-time Secretary of State for Health) and a former Labour Sports Minister, arguing that the location is 'a precious local and national asset which should be preserved in the public domain, and because of its sensitive position inspires great loyalty'. What's this got to do with the price of tea in China?

Why should the building be preserved as a memorial to those dissected within its walls or to the frogs who suffered silently while their gastrocnemii were electrocuted, not to mention the students who have been humiliated in the name of education? If it can't be reopened as a medical school, and we are told that it cannot, then why not invest in it a useful purpose? To turn the words around of the petitioned letter to the Council of King's College, the widest public *would* be best served by accepting the Aga Khan's offer.

Whatever the eventual fate of her carcass, St Thomas's Hospital Medical School is extinct. Centuries of tradition and stories of penises on the Underground engulfed by a God-awful set of initials: GKT.

A couple of years ago I happened to find myself in one of these undignified creations. It was at Imperial, and I had been invited to attend a symposium on pre-eclampsia. The guest speaker was meant to be Sarath de Alwis Seneviratne, my buddy, but for some reason he was unable to make it and so had been substituted by none other than Madam Chop Chop, by this time a consultant obstetrician at a London hospital, a post which she continues to hold.

I mingled with colleagues in the interlude and after a while I found myself facing the old girl herself. We made small talk and I noticed that she was trying discreetly to read the corporate-sponsored, conference-style name badge pinned to my jacket. She neither recognised nor remembered me.

We chatted amiably and when I paused for a moment to reflect upon a question she asked about my line of work, she waited, smiling and patient, for me to respond.

13

The rum was inexpensive and had a rich, fruity flavour. It went well with the simple lunch of ackee and freshly boiled potatoes. Jamaica − hot, tropical, beautiful, memorable, an idyllic location to unwind from the toll of medical life. Far away from patients and even further from the tick-box, target-driven culture that epitomises the Government's approach to the NHS. A chance, then, to relax.

Roopal and I had hired a taxi for the day; we had visited beaches, caves and coastal villages before climbing Dunn's River Falls and now we were drinking rum and feeling quite hearty. At 1 o'clock, tired but fulfilled, we set off for our hotel in Falmouth. The Jamaican at the wheel hummed quietly as we hurtled along in his jalopy. His face was expressionless but he was, at least, sober.

I was drifting in and out of a hazy slumber, twice waking abruptly to hypnagogic hallucinations, the startling jolts that come in that twilight state immediately before sleep. To most people it's the sensation of going over the edge of a cliff, say; we've all seen the fellow passenger on a train nodding off, only to waken with a sudden jerk. The converse to a hypnagogic hallucination is a hypnopompic one, occurring in the state immediately preceding waking up. A dream might be punctuated by a regular beeping noise and the subject wakes to find his alarm clock sounding, exactly in time to the noise in the dream. The dream could have been about a meal in a restaurant. The waiter brings the food and then a bottle of wine. As he drives the corkscrew into the neck of the bottle, there is a shrill beep accompanying each turn of his wrist. The dreamer wakes up to hear his alarm clock sounding. In actual fact he is stirred awake *because* of the beeping signal and has a hypnopompic hallucination involving the waiter's action. Fascinating stuff, eh?

Where was I? Yes – riding along the road in Jamaica with Roopal awake and me drifting off. Certainly neither of us can recall the motorbike overtaking our taxi nor the horrific sequence of events that followed. The bike must have swung out to pass us, perhaps giving us a wide berth in order to avoid the many cavernous pot holes. The head-on collision with the truck coming the other way was, by then, unavoidable.

The mess is, today, still vivid in my mind. The rider of the motorbike, an American tourist in his twenties, was lying in the centre of the road with the mangled remains of his machine wrapped around him. His girlfriend was in the plantation on the opposite side of the carriageway. Debris from their hired motorcycle was strewn across the uneven concrete, and the flesh of hundreds of ripe water-melons shed from the truck mingled with blood from both victims. Miraculously, the melon man was unhurt.

I clambered out of the taxi and made towards the girl in the field. She had an obvious bimalleolar (both inner and outer sides) ankle fracture with a deep cut across one side, the inner aspect of the ankle. Shards of bone poked through her open wound.

There was also a large haematoma (bruise) over the back of her scalp from which blood was spurting forth. The girl was conscious but disorientated, unaware of her name, whereabouts or what had happened. Her boyfriend, also conscious, appeared to have no external injuries but he was complaining of chest pain and a heavy sensation in his left loin.

Roopal, a nurse, tore pieces from our beach towels to make pressure dressings which she held to the girl's ankle and head. We were in the middle of bloody nowhere and, apart from the van driver and inimical cab driver, there were no signs of nearby civilisation. I realised, in despair, that we would have to transport our two 'patients' in our taxi. Our driver, who refused to start his engine until money had changed hands, eventually agreed to help once a worthy price had been agreed for the use of his hardly suitable vehicle. And so the bumpy journey began.

By the time we had reached the small hospital on the island's north coast, the girl's level of consciousness had deteriorated. The hospital was scruffy and unwelcoming, and the single casualty officer (a Caucasian from Belgium, I think) was uninterested in both patients. There were just a couple of rooms off the main entrance and a handful of wooden huts lay outside. Perhaps, I thought, it was a clinic and not a hospital.

I introduced myself to the Belgian doctor and described the new arrivals' injuries. He grunted and wandered nonchalantly over to where they now lay. I then watched in disbelief as he prepared to suture the girl's ankle: a fracture with a laceration over it – a so-called 'open' or compound fracture – is infected and must always be thoroughly cleansed, preferably in an operating theatre. And what about an X-ray first? And, hey, what about the head injury? A fractured ankle takes second place to trauma to the skull!

The Belgian sensed my disapproval and explained that the radiographer only visited weekly to perform non-urgent X-rays. He said the hospital didn't have facilities to irrigate compound fractures, although to do so would, he agreed, be a good idea, and that he was going to do what he always did: sew up the laceration, bung on a plaster cast, and give some antibiotics to prevent an infection from setting in. He reassured me that her head would 'hopefully settle overnight' and, all being well, he would discharge her the next day.

What about the bloke? I asked. Her boyfriend was moaning in pain from his chest and he was weeing blood. The Belgian thought he had cracked a few ribs and reckoned that the blood in the urine resulted from penile trauma incurred from the impact with the bike.

I wanted arterial blood gases, a chest X-ray and an intravenous urogram done. Possibly an MRI scan too. As for the girl, she needed a brain scan, neurological observation and, later, internal fixation of her bimalleolar ankle fracture in an operating theatre. They both needed intravenous fluids – unavailable in the small hospital – and I suddenly felt dejected and, unusually, defeated.

I asked the Belgian about a transfer to a larger hospital. He told me that Montego Bay, the nearest town, was sixty miles away. He was reluctant and told me that I was interfering, which I suppose I was, but I knew that it was our only chance. Without asking him for permission, I injected some local anaesthetic into the girl's ankle and then went outside to negotiate with our taxi man for him to take the two injured tourists to Montego Bay where (I hoped) there would be a better-equipped hospital. It was a no-go situation. His price was exorbitant and far greater than the sum of our Jamaican currency. I showed him the collection of coins and notes mustered from my pockets and the Americans' backpack, but he shook his head.

Melon man, who had followed in his truck to the hospital, came to the rescue. He said he felt so bad about what had happened that he would be only too pleased to take them to Montego Bay. He discarded the few melons that had remained on the back of his truck and helped me to lift the Americans on, one at a time. The Jamaican nurses were wonderful: they provided mattresses and bedding to make the ride bearable, and much to the disapprobation of the Belgian, we set off.

The young American man had, indeed, fractured some ribs – three in all. The blood issuing from his penis was from a serious injury to his right kidney, diagnosed by an intravenous urogram performed by the emergency team at Montego Bay. His girlfriend underwent brain surgery later that evening for an intracerebral bleed. She made a full recovery although walks with a limp.

In her annual Christmas greetings a year or so ago she announced her engagement, though not to the rider of the motorbike. She has said that she won't ever forgive him.

14

It was an Indian summer's day in September 2001 when Robert, my eldest, started school. He looked grown-up in his new uniform. In his preoccupation with getting ready, he didn't notice when his favourite cartoon character flitted across the television screen and then suddenly vanished amidst an unhealthy 'pop': the TV had packed up. Our Sony television, a wedding present in 1993, had served us faithfully (if a television can do such a thing) until that morning. Roopal shrugged as I turned it off, and we thought no more about it. There were more pressing things to attend to.

Robert nervously eyed the clock although he couldn't yet comprehend the numbers on its face, and Roopal acknowledged that we should set off. Best not be late, she had said. I grabbed my camera and we walked the short journey to Rokeby School. There are few who forget their first day at school even if they then can't remember any subsequent day. I remember my own very clearly and that September morning I relived it as my wife and I accompanied our four-year-old son down the gravelled drive to the main school building: I too went to Rokeby and my first day in September 1972 seemed as if it had taken place just a few years previously.

Back home, in the strange emptiness that followed, I picked up a newspaper but there wasn't much of interest. I had taken a week off from the surgery and for just an instant I wished that I was at work. At least the day goes quickly when you're seeing patients. Roopal flicked the TV on but nothing happened. Of course – it was broken.

She telephoned the engineer, who to our amazement said he would come around later that day. Sure enough, sometime in the afternoon, with Robert now home from school, the repair man fiddled with the innards of our TV. He tugged and then twisted a few wires and suddenly the set burst into life, its now-functioning screen revealing the most horrific film. It was far too vivid for daytime viewing.

An aeroplane was heading for a skyscraper and we watched as it crashed into the side of the building.

'*Towering Inferno*, most like,' the engineer laughed. Robert buried his head in the sofa cushions. The engineer grimaced a sort of apology and changed channels by tapping his metal screwdriver across the soldered connections on the remote's circuit board.

'That's odd,' he said, scratching his head with the

remote control. 'It's the same.' The television screen showed the identical sequence of film although the engineer lingered long enough for us to see fire and smoke billow from the stricken skyscraper. He changed it again, and then again, but the 'film' was repeated on each channel, with only the commentary differing.

Much has been written and said in the aftermath of the September 11th attacks on the World Trade Center and the Pentagon, including a plethora of reports which unreasonably tarnish the entire Muslim faith. Significant in my mind, however, is the need for the West to understand Islam. I mean *really* understand it. Most Britons have a feeble grasp of any culture other than their own and have no shame at their pathetic lack of empathy with those who follow the Muslim faith. Being introduced to the tradition and beautiful heritage of a contrasting culture, as I was to Hinduism when I married Roopal, is more than an education; it is a cultivation.

I have patients from each and every religion, and so I welcomed the report by the Open Society Institute, a think-tank set up by the philanthropist George Soros, which says that Arabic should be offered as a foreign language in schools, alongside French, German and Spanish. The report, written by a lecturer in international human rights at Durham University, also recommends that information about equality and anti-discrimination should be included in the citizenship curriculum.

Londoners, indeed any civilised persons who happen to be in the capital, visiting an Islamic culture centre such as that proposed by the Aga Khan on the old St Thomas's site, would be partaking of a privileged experience. If it were to go ahead, and at this stage it is by no means certain, then I would wish to be first in the queue.

Eric Finch abhorred anyone whose ailment he perceived to be self-inflicted. I remember him, on a ward round at St Thomas's, at the bedside of a patient with an alcohol-related illness.

'Alcohol,' he rants, 'is the cause of so much suffering. So much misery.' Then, with typically stern expression, he addresses one of the firm. 'Professor Peters,' he booms. 'This man has a cardiomyopathy. Heard of that one? Ah, good. Enlighten us then. Start with aetiology. The Aetiology, Ladies and Gentlemen, of Cardiomyopathy.'

Tania dutifully recites the rhyme:

> *Heredity, sex and age,*
> *Occupation, race and clime,*
> *The ills that men are subject to –*
> *The vices of our time.*

'Yes vices, professor,' grunts Finch, with no more than a hint of praise for Tania Peters discernible in his voice. 'Vices. Oh where would we all be were it not for vices? I would suggest that this hospital would not be here today had not the corruptions and immoralities of successive generations kept it here. *Keeping* it here.' Finch shifts his glare to each of us in turn, enjoying the attention he always managed to command. We, in turn, are entranced: the captive and captured entourage of his sacred ward rounds. Interruptions or, worse, inattention were just too perilous for words.

I'm positioned at the end of the human arc, and his narrowed eyes momentarily meet mine before falling on the crumpled patient before us.

'Yes my friends,' he continues, 'there shall always be those who succumb to the vices of our time, and to them we are thankful.' He pauses for a second before continuing. 'Thankful for ensuring we are prosperous in knowledge and wisdom.'

'Hear! hear!' says Nabhi Shah, and everyone stifles a laugh. Everyone, that is, but Finch and his patient.

November 2001 and I'm in the surgery on a Saturday afternoon catching up with my paperwork. I am pleased with the volume of solicitors' reports, patients' mortgage applications and referral letters I have cleared, and I have even managed to read a couple of medical journals. One contains an obituary on a long-retired St Thomas's consultant. 'A fine teacher and a fine performer, but he was a vain and arrogant man.' *Performer?* I read on: 'It was in the clinics of St Thomas's Hospital that he performed best, perfecting the demonstration of his overbearing showmanship to the cost, perhaps, of his treatment of patients: it could be said that consideration of the latter was but a minor detail in a long and enviable career.' I pause to reflect on this. 'Enviable' doesn't seem the right word.

Window open, fresh coffee to sustain me; the place is strangely empty without the patients and staff to create the usual hustle and bustle. I'm lost in a world of my own until the sense of oblivion is fractured by the doorbell. The shrill noise is a sudden and unwelcome interruption. When the surgery is closed, it's closed. As I walk towards the window to catch sight of who is outside, it rings a second time. This time, however, the person keeps their finger pressed on the buzzer, and the noise is continuous, resonating around the building. The ringing continues but I can't see who's outside. They are so close to the front door as to be invisible from the first-floor windows.

I'm off duty but the feeling of urgency is palpable. Maybe someone is injured, possibly from an accident on the main road by the surgery. Or maybe someone is choking or has collapsed: the list of could-be's is endless.

As I approach the front door, the shouting begins.

'Open the farking dooer! Open the dorrer! OPEN THE FUCKING DOOR!'

The words are slurred, unformed.

'Who is it?' I ask in my ever-so-polite, eager-to-please voice.

'Nether you fer-farrking moind,' continues the shouter. 'And don't even fink of cor-ling the police.' Through the large square pane of glass in the front door, which seems now so inviting to a would-be intruder, I can see that the man is unkempt and is staggering. He has a bottle of beer in one hand, with the other hand lashing out with each sentence as if in wild and crude gesticulation. From his dishevelled face stare inflamed orbits – sore, certainly, but their cast vacant.

Again I ask what the matter is. I don't recognise him as one of my patients.

'Diashy Pam,' comes the reply.

'Who? Oh, you mean *diazepam*?' I say, interpreting his request for Valium.

'Yessh. Now-er. Now-er. NOW!'

The shouting goes on for what feels like an age although is probably no more than a few minutes. I'm alone in the building and realise that it would be foolhardy to let him in. Not because I'm not his GP, but because diazepam is not a drug that we stock in the surgery. Life-saving medication for heart attacks and anaphylaxis, yes, but not standard pharmaceutical supplies like antibiotics, pain killers or sedatives such as diazepam. And, above all, fuelling an addict's habit adds to the burning fire of his craving. No better than giving Finch's cardiomyopathic chap a bottle of Châteauneuf-du-Pape, however well-intentioned one's gesture.

'I'm afraid I don't have any diazepam,' I say. 'We don't keep any drugs on the premises.'

'You bar-sted! You farking open the door,' says our man.

'I really can't help you.'

'The chemist's got it, so give us a scrippy.' I thought he might accompany this request with a little smile but, no, just the same vacant eyes: neither hard nor cold in expression, just empty and devoid of sentiment.

I have no intention of *prescribing* him diazepam and, fortunately, we keep the prescription, or 'script', pads locked up when the surgery is closed. I can't help feeling sorry for the man on the doorstep. He looks weary and unloved and alone. The absence of emotion in both his demeanour and requests belies the real sense of desperation he must feel, like the starving beggar in need of nourishment but who asks each passing stranger with less and less vigour, knowing that his pleas will be ignored, until his expression becomes vacuous and wanting of animation.

I turn from my place inside the front door and go to the small kitchen at the back of the house. The remains of what was once a hatch, now sealed and mostly plastered over, are the only reminder that this was once a pantry. In days long ago this would have been the domain of servants, busily preparing a tray of coffee for Dr Milne as he completed his morning surgery.

I make a cup of tea with plenty of sugar and, together with some biscuits brought in by a grateful patient, leave them on the step outside the back door.

When the man at the front of the building sees me once more approaching through the glass in the door, he resumes his doorbell-accompanied monotone discourse.

'Look,' I say, smiling but firm, 'I can't help you with booze or diazepam – but if you come back on Monday, when we're open, you can pick up some leaflets on local agencies that can provide help. You know, guidance and support. Please. And I've left some tea and biscuits at the back of the surgery. Please help yourself.'

The man utters a few words, inaudible – but I assume, naïvely, of gratitude – and staggers round to the side of the surgery building.

I make my way upstairs. Back in my office, I reflect on whether I have done the right thing. Certainly I was right not to prescribe anything and wise not to let him in. I watch from the window as he makes his way along Richmond Road, the bustling thoroughfare leading to the town centre. His bottle of beer is gripped in one hand but in the other, now, is held a gleaming white mug. I see him stop every so often and take a large gulp from the mug, the tea perhaps a welcome change from beer. He must strike a strange pose: almost destitute and yet a choice of contrasting sops to imbibe.

Deep down, though, I feel only despair. For what have I really, *really*, done to help this man? Nothing, is the honest answer. He was in need and asking me, a doctor, for help, and I turned him away. Finch had said we owe our existence to those whose lives stray from the straight and narrow. But are doctors grateful for this beneficence? We show too readily the face of criticism and scorn, rather than one of pity and empathy.

For a few fleeting moments I see St Thomas's main central corridor as it stretches elegantly away from my window – and beyond. The pedestrians are the doctors, porters and patients; likewise three women, perhaps sisters in the blood sense, three ward sisters, resplendent in their imposing blue and white spotted uniforms; children in their push chairs, the frightened patients, young and old, en route to outpatient clinics. Everyone is about their own business, engrossed in thoughts but for their minds alone.

The scene contains an odd-looking chap with a mug of tea: yet he is as much a part of this corridor culture as he is apart from it. He is no different from the tormented souls that traverse passageways of hospitals worldwide, invisible and insignificant to the purposeful.

My mind permits the return of normality. I can just make out the man's form, tiny by virtue of its distance, and my eyes cling to the image until it is fatefully devoured by the mass of colours and shapes that make up the town.

★   ★   ★

I've known rivers:
I've known rivers ancient as the world and older
than the flow of human blood in human veins.

Langston Hughes
1902–67

Far and near, these are times of innovation and change. The world has been transformed, even in the short time since the horrors of September 11th, and it would be rash to predict what the next couple of years might bring. One is aware of turbulent changes in healthcare and the erosion of more and more of the old and familiar landmarks.

At St Thomas's Hospital, at least, a much-loved and memorable way of life remains – the main 'central' corridor. Trammelled and truncated by the vicissitudes of successive alien architects, it has somehow managed to survive and stay as much the life-stream within as the River Thames without. Under the watchful gaze of Edward VI, the boy-king who ensured the resurrection of St Thomas's eleven years after its closure by his father, and whose statue guards the hospital's entrance, the new front hall still has that special bustle of expectant activity as countless numbers come and go to heal, be healed or just hope. The famous corridor is still long enough to be a vibrant thoroughfare and meeting place, despite lifts, levels, stairways and a long-silenced paternoster.

The medical students, alas, have gone, but the motley of patients, nurses, doctors, visitors, helpers and all those who make the 'caring profession' possible, ebbs and flows from morning until night. If only statues could speak...

Somewhere, hurrying to a clinic, ward or laboratory, there is someone who is on the threshold of a discovery. There is a house officer, destined to be a great consultant of tomorrow. There is a poor soul who has come but will never return.

Faces come and go endlessly, like the tide. Mingling in this maelstrom of humanity are the good and the bad, the strong and the weak, the sick in body and the sick in mind. Further still can be found the flotsam and jetsam of life, conveyed by river and corridor alike as each proceeds to its destination. An uncertain end point, so to speak, of the flowing passageway's journey to the estuary – unknown waters, unknown territory, in fact a vast unknowness.

Sweet Thames, run softly, till I end my song.

Edmund Spenser
c. 1552–99

15

A righteous man regardeth the life of his beast: but the tender mercies of the wicked are cruel.

Bible: Proverbs

In the town where I practise there is a poster which depicts the bust – one hopes that this is the correct word, for it shows the head and neck – of a hen. The eyes have been blacked out by a solid dark rectangle superimposed on the print, as one might see on a medical photograph to preserve the anonymity and thus confidentiality of its subject. The poster advertises a restaurant where one of the dishes, I presume, is called 'wicked chicken'.

There is a tendency to 'beef up' (if you'll excuse the pun) a culinary creation by the prefix 'wicked' – hence 'wicked chocolate pudding', or 'wickedly naughty treacle sponge', and so on.

Anyway, back to the poster. The photograph has been printed to look intentionally grainy so that one might think it has been reproduced from CCTV footage; for added effect the time and date has been printed in mock digital font in the top right-hand corner. This, together with the grainy image and shielded eyes, all conspire to make the poor chicken appear as a wanted criminal.

I eat meat but I respect the animals that form part of my diet. I do not make fun of them nor do I deride them: to do so is insulting.

The legend underneath the image says:

'Wicked Chicken' spotted at new style T.G.I. Friday's.

Desmond Morris, the English anthropologist, said in 1990: 'Death may be inevitable but cruelty is not. If we must eat meat, then we must ensure that the animals we kill for our food live the best possible lives before they die.' I do not think that mockery contributes to the quality of an animal's life. The poster remains.

**The American
Restaurant & Bar**

T.G.I. Friday's, Whitbread Court, Houghton Hall Office Park, Porz Avenue, Dunstable LU5 5XE
Telephone: (01582) 424200 Fax: (01582) 844888

28 October 2002

Dear Dr Barrie

Thank you for your letter concerning our Wicked Chicken advertisement, which our Kingston restaurant has forwarded to me for attention.

I do apologise for the offence, which this advertisement has caused you and would like to advise you that we are planning to replace this with an alternative poster. At this stage I am not able to say exactly when this will take place but our advertising agency are giving it their urgent attention.

Yours sincerely

**Joe Boyle
Marketing Director**

16

A man must serve his time to every trade
Save censure – critics all are ready made.

Lord Byron
1788–1824

Christmas 2001 came and went without much ado; compared with the extravagant festivities of the millennium commemoration one year earlier, the New Year celebrations that hailed the arrival of 2002 were muted. Besides, a doctor was required to cover the 'out of hours' service and it fell to local GPs to work six-hour shifts on Christmas Day, Boxing Day and New Year's Day. So after what seemed the shortest of breaks, I was back in the surgery trying to cope with the hordes of ill folk wishing to be seen. *Wishing* to be seen. *Wanting* to be seen. And, in Mrs Blackall's case, *demanding* to be seen.

'I must see Dr Barrie right away,' she told the receptionist. No 'please' in her request; not even the grateful smile of anticipation.

'I'm sorry,' replied my receptionist, 'but Dr Barrie is fully booked until the seventh of January. Is it something urgent?'

'Of course it is,' the woman said impatiently, 'otherwise I wouldn't be here, would I?'

The receptionist, ignoring the rhetorical question, tried to be complaisant. 'We have an emergency surgery this morning,' she soothed. 'I can fit you in there, if you like.'

'Only if Dr Barrie is doing it. The surgery, that is. Only if he's doing it,' scowled Mrs Blackall.

'I'm afraid you can't choose the doctor if it's an emergency. All four doctors take a turn to run the emergency surgery.'

'So whose turn does it happen to be this week?' said Mrs Blackall. Strange how anger can give way to sarcasm.

'Umm, Dr … Barrie,' the receptionist admitted.

'So that's all right then. Why the fuss?'

Mrs Blackall plonked herself in a chair before the receptionist had had a chance to answer, never mind invite her to take a seat in the waiting room – that rite of passage signifying 'approval' of one's appointment.

As far as Mrs Blackall was concerned, her condition warranted an urgent appointment and, not content with waiting a few days like the majority of far sicker patients, she had exercised 'her right' to be seen the same day.

Her right. Words that I came to despise as a GP. *I want to be referred to a consultant because it's my right.* Or, *I want to go on the sick, it's my right.* And worse still, *It's my right to have a home visit.*

Wrong, wrong, wrong! Nobody has a 'right' to be seen the same day. Nor demand incapacity benefit. And certainly not to insist that a doctor pay a home visit. If a patient is unwell or suffering then of course a doctor should see them. Any doctor. A drowning man would not cry out for a particular lifeboat man to save him.

But Mrs Blackall wanted an urgent appointment specifically with me. A most demanding woman who, much like a spoilt child, got her way.

'So how can I help?' I asked. To youngsters I usually say, 'Fire away'; to those who have been attending the practice for years I might say: 'So *now* what have you gone and done?' But Mrs Blackall bristles and I can't be doing with any of that.

'My husband is having an affair,' came her reply. The imperious woman raised her eyebrows on the last word, hoping I would share the shock of this astounding scandal. I, however, sighed – bored and uninterested – although I sensed that she perceived the sigh as one of dismay for her husband's misdemeanour.

'I found out in October. I was in the bank paying some

cheques in. There was a queue and I bumped into a friend, you know how it is, and –'

'But it's January now...' I interjected. 'What's made this such an urgent problem?'

'Urgent? What do you mean, Dr Barrie?'

'You asked at reception for an urgent appointment.'

'Did I?' Mrs Blackall sounded surprised. 'Oh, so I did! I must have got into a muddle. You know what it's like at the reception desk. A cross-examination just to get an appointment to see you. So where was I? Oh yes,' she continued, 'I remember. The bank. So there I was in the bank and I bumped into my friend and we got talking. Anyway, she had seen my husband with this other lady. Hatti says they were kissing and –'

'Hatti?' I asked.

'Hatti, the friend I met in the bank,' said Mrs Blackall impatiently. 'She, I mean *Hatti*, saw them kissing in the park over by the river. Saw them twice, she did. On different days. And,' she said, lowering her voice in a knowing sort of way, ' *that* was back in October.'

Like the wise old woodpecker of the one-time children's television series *Bagpuss* who jumps down from his book-end, I felt like raising my hand up and saying, Stop all this! Stop it right now! What, my dear Mrs Blackall, has any of this got to do with me? How on earth do you expect a doctor to be able to help you? I've got a waiting room full of really sick patients: men with chest pain; children with fevers; and babies refusing their feeds. And you, Mrs Blackall, are blathering on about a woman called Hatti who has seen your errant husband kissing someone in a park by the Thames. *Come on, Mrs B!*

Instead I said: 'I can see all that, Mrs Blackall, but time is pressing on. What is it exactly that I can do to help?'

'Help? Oh you can't do anything, Dr Barrie,' ventured Mrs Blackall. 'I told my husband outright in October. Let me see … yes, that's more than eight weeks ago. I told him straight up. You've been seen, I said, by my friend Hatti. I said that Hatti said that she'd seen you slobbering over some girl in the park, and he said he hadn't. He said that it was a mistake. Must have been someone that wasn't him, just looked like him. But no, I said. I said that Hatti said…'

God help me! I thought. Please, not the whole story all over again.

'Are you depressed?' As soon as I'd said it I realised that I had broken all the rules in the book. Depression, as with any mental illness, is a diagnosis of subtleness. Open-ended questions; listening astutely for little hints in the answers: cues in the history; and intimations and suggestions discerned from the clinical presentation – making a diagnosis of depression is an art.

'Goodness, Dr Barrie. Whatever do you mean?'

'I was wondering where this is leading to, that's all. I am conscious of those in the waiting room, Mrs Blackall.'

'But why should I be depressed?' she asked, clearly astonished by my question.

'Well, isn't that why you're here?' I asked 'You're upset and—'

'Certainly not! I'm not upset. So, as I was saying, I told my husband that Hatti had seen the two of them in the park. Well, he turned round...'

Such a start to a busy 'emergency' surgery is always unsettling. I tried to block out the vertiginous image of her revolving husband in order that my brain might hatch a plan to procure her rapid exit from my room. No wonder that so many doctors scribble out a prescription for some or other medicament, thrust it across the desk, and then walk the patient to the door. The consultation is terminated (the main goal) and the patient is happy (feels vindicated, especially in front of the receptionist, that he – in this case, *she* – was sufficiently ill for the doctor to give some 'get-better' pills).

So what's the answer? It's all down to personality. Not of the patient, but of the doctor. A kind, caring and giving doctor will attract far more patients than the miserable, grumpy doctor who is devoid of a bedside manner. But it's more than just *numbers* of patients. The first kind of doctor *lures* patients: the sad and lonely; the socially destitute; those who don't want to help themselves: in a word, the *heartsinks*.

Conscientious, caring, respected, kindhearted, popular: all words that might define a good doctor. Qualities, it might be said, to aspire to in general practice. But no, these are patients' words. These are adjectives that a man on the street might use to describe his notion of a perfect doctor. We've all met people who think the world of their GP. He's absolutely wonderful, they say. Such a *nice* doctor, you know. Always there for you. Aha! *Always there for you*. What they mean is that they bug him mercilessly. For the pitiful capitation fee received by that particular doctor, our awe-struck friend is a frequent attender. A needle in the poor doctor's side. A bane, certainly, and perhaps a heartsink to boot. But has such a wonderful doctor.

Now try asking a doctor the same question. Ask him to list a few of the attributes that make a doctor a 'good' doctor. Clever, he will probably say. Astute. Knowledge-able. And smart, quick-witted, up-to-date, clear-sighted, perceptive. All qualities, he will say with envy, of a good doctor.

A few months after Mrs Blackall's visit to the surgery, a GP in Cornwall experienced only too painfully what it meant to be popular. Dr Lucinda Macdonald was described by her patients as 'a lovely, popular and caring doctor, very giving with her time.' But their praise came too late, for their words were spoken in tribute after she had committed suicide. At the inquest, in June 2002, her fiancé said that 'she could not reduce her devotion to the needs of patients'. In other words, she cared too much.

In my days as a junior doctor at Epsom Hospital, I worked alongside a doctor who one night was called to see a patient on the ward. As she walked past the front of the doctors' mess she found a body lying at the foot of the tall building. Her shock was magnified when she saw that the untidy and lifeless figure was a fellow hospital doctor. He had been on duty all weekend and, after a gruelling day's work on Monday, had injected himself with insulin and then flung himself from the window of his dingy room. The whole hospital community was aghast, with doctors and nurses silently mourning his death. A couple of years later a trainee GP, in her twenties and with a vocation spent caring for the needs of her community stretching before her, committed suicide.

They say that doctors have the dubious pleasure of

choosing one of many ways to depart this world – and the young GP injected herself with an intravenous bolus of potassium chloride. Again I lamented the loss of a friend and colleague. I knew her but not so well that I ever saw the digs where her final act took place; yet for many months I could not rid my mind of a haunting re-enactment of her last few moments. I pictured, perhaps inaccurately, the girl alone, the epitome of misery and sadness and unhappiness, as she administered her fatal injection; life so unbearable that this was the unique solution. Then the mini-scene in my head is over; the curtain has come down. There is no happy ending nor, poignantly, any gain.

After the hospital doctor at Epsom took his own life, his father embarked upon a relentless fight to bring about change so that another family would not have to suffer the devastation of losing a son or daughter to an indifferent NHS – and indifferent public.

It's a sad fact that the few patients who lean so heavily on their 'wonderful and caring' doctor throughout his professional life – mercilessly and at no cost to themselves – then saddle their selfish needs on the new incumbent. They've sucked and sucked and sucked until the doctor can take no more: the doctor retires, or dies, or resigns, and the patients may or may not shed a tear. But the next day they're back in their usual spot in the surgery. Half leech, half vulture: they are unchanged and unrepentant.

I admired the efforts of the dead doctor's father for he sought urgent discussions with the British Medical Association and General Medical Council. He spoke with patients' representatives. He made it his mission to improve the working conditions and morale of junior doctors whose accommodation, on-call facilities and leisure amenities were at that time notoriously bad. Hours worked were excessively long and a remedy was imperative to prevent the needless loss of life.

And yet bringing about change seemed impossible. Consultants, like the surgeons at Kingston, prevaricated their way through the red tape, keeping the Government happy whilst stitching up the juniors looking after their precious patients. When things went well the consultant would be there at the bedside, waving aside the praise lavished upon them. It's nothing, they would say. Really nothing, don't mention it.

But if things went wrong, it was a very different side we saw. Oh, but Miss Smith, they would proclaim, you must speak with my house officer. After all, they would add with an embarrassed chuckle, it wasn't *me* who messed up your intravenous drip at three in the morning, was it? And then later, to me, in a quiet but thinly-veiled threat, Don't you think you should go and apologise to Lucie Smith in Bed 3? Yes? There's a good chap!

But that would all end with the New Deal, wouldn't it? Virginia Bottomley had undertaken to cut the intolerable hours worked by young doctors. Life would improve; we would be refreshed from a decent night's sleep; and patient care would not be compromised. Or so I thought. I remember my experiences at Kingston a year or so earlier, and the incorrigible behaviour of the consultant surgeon. You can't stop people such as this. Like the charade put on when Knight-Smith from the Task Force visited. The surgeon pulled the wool over his eyes all right.

My busy days – when I only occasionally caught sight of my lodgings – are long over, but the hours worked are still long, and patient demand remains at an all-time high. Despondency amongst doctors is rife, and fewer school leavers are choosing to enter the medical profession. Moreover, many doctors wish they had not become doctors in the first place. Suicide in the medical profession, and amongst general practitioners in particular, is rising and the sorrow felt when we fail to detect the signs of despair and hopelessness in a patient is far greater when the death is of a fellow doctor.

Another 'doctor suicide' is that of Dawn Harris, a thirty-eight-year-old GP who practised in Bolton and who hanged herself in August 2003. She was found by her husband, who later said: 'She had become depressed because of the stress of the job she longed to do but also because she couldn't do more to help heal people. She cared for everyone and was totally dedicated.' In other words, Dr Harris killed herself because she was unable to care for her patients as much as she had wanted. But this wasn't her fault: surely it's that of the patients who had unreasonable expectations of her?

Medicine can often seem an unending battle against illness, disease and horrendous affliction: the battle is more bloody because we *too* are distressed by what we see. Doctors in general practice are emotionally isolated, more so if we do not share our experiences with colleagues; the victims of a suicide inevitably include those colleagues who are painfully aware of their failed moral obligation to the dead doctor.

Lucinda Macdonald was the jewel in the crown of family medicine. Likewise Dr Dawn Harris. But each woman's flawless devotion to her patients meant that she worried too much about them. Too caring, too conscientious, too good. Too good, in the end, for their own good. Their patients loved them and killed them. Just as one day Mrs Blackall will probably kill me.

17

Ayesha was twenty-four and overjoyed to be pregnant. She and her husband had been trying to conceive since their marriage four years earlier, and I had arranged countless investigations in an attempt to discover the cause of her infertility. A childless relationship can result from medical problems in either partner, but we knew that the 'fault' lay with Ayesha for her husband had excellent gametes. Detailed analyses on his semen had shown impeccable results for sperm shape, motility and total count.

'There must be *something* you can do, doctor,' she had implored. I talked her through the stages of *in vitro* fertilisation and wrote to the gynaecologist at our local assisted conception unit. A year later she sat in my consulting room, beaming from ear to ear.

'Your embryo was transferred in the second week of August. So that makes you … um … [I twiddled the dial on my gestation calculator] yes that makes you nine weeks.' I notified the maternity unit and our surgery-based midwife. Ayesha thanked me and left. Her happiness was infectious.

She came to see me for regular antenatal checks and

everything progressed smoothly. The Easter following her IVF treatment, her husband, a reticent if not somewhat aloof sort of chap, visited the surgery to drop off the familiar green and white delivery note.

'Three in the morning,' he smiled. 'All went fine. We've called him Rijul – it means "innocent" in my language.'

'How's Ayesha?' I asked.

'Oh, she's doing great. Tired, but great.'

'And little Rijul? He's OK?' I felt pleased for both of them.

'Perfect,' he replied. 'I'm headed for the hospital right now, in fact. Ayesha needed a few things from home. I was passing, so I thought I would deliver the hospital note.'

I watched him drive away. I had probably spoken more with him just then that at any stage in the past. I grinned to myself in shared understanding at the happiness of newly-found fatherhood. When Robert, my first son, was born in 1996 – at the same hospital as Rijul – I too experienced the wonderment and pleasure that all fathers will recognise.

Rijul came for his various checks, and Ayesha, like many new mothers, was a common sight at the surgery, in need of reassurance that he was a bonny and healthy baby.

One day, I think when Rijul was about eighteen months, she asked to see me urgently. She was anxious and unsettled.

'He's getting at me,' she said quietly. 'Won't let me do anything.'

I waited.

'Nothing,' she continued. 'He's always out. He says work is busy but I don't believe him. Rijul cries and he tell me I stop him making a noise.'

'For how long has this been happening?' I asked gently.

'Four or five months, maybe it is more,' Ayesha sobbed, the tears rolling down her face.

She told me how her husband had become distant and uncommunicative; I listened while she recounted how he had become distrustful of her, unloving and uninterested in both her and their son. I thought that most likely he was exhibiting signs of paranoia, but how can one prove this without an examination, and to suggest this to him would surely spill the beans that she had spoken with me.

I called a meeting later that day with my partners and the one person I hoped would be a key player in my strategy — Jill, my health visitor. Jill has an astute knack of picking up vibes that others cannot discern; she quickly gets the 'feel' of a tricky situation and has enormous practical skill in problem-solving. She agreed, at once, to do what a health visitor does best: visit.

She was disturbed to find that matters were more fraught than the picture Ayesha had painted. Her husband had confiscated all her personal papers, such as her birth certificate, passport, cheque book and so on, saying that they were safer in his office at work, and had removed all the loose change and bank notes from their flat.

'So how does she go shopping?' I asked.

'Ah,' said Jill, 'she doesn't. Her husband has to take her and he pays for whatever provisions are required. She and Rijul don't exactly go without. There's plenty of food in the fridge. But she's got no independence, no life of her own.'

I listened carefully to Jill's explanation. 'But surely she can telephone her friends?' I said. 'Or her mother?'

'No, you don't get it,' said Jill. 'Her husband has removed all the telephones. He has a mobile telephone which she can use, but he keeps it with him so she can only use it in the evening when he comes home. And,' she added, 'in his presence.'

It was essential to get Ayesha's husband in for a chat. I telephoned him but there was no reply. Of course, I realised, the telephone sets had been removed! Twice I visited but on each occasion Ayesha was there alone, unhappy and perturbed by my presence. I decided instead to write to him, saying that I wished to speak with him in connection with Rijul's vaccination schedule.

'The months have flown since he was born,' he said in my surgery a couple of weeks later. The man appeared relaxed and happy. We chatted about the stresses of parenthood. The need, as he put it, for time to oneself.

'The importance of *working* at a relationship shared by a child,' I agreed. But I could discern nothing remarkable. He talked, in fact we talked. His speech was spontaneous and his thoughts reactive, their content appropriate.

'No sign then of mental illness?' Jill asked after he had gone.

'Nope,' I said, 'nothing. Seems a pretty straightforward chap.'

A week or so later, Ayesha was back. She was tired, she said, because she had to walk to the surgery. Rijul, not yet two, had to be carried. She had no money, she said, for the bus or to use a public telephone. She couldn't call her mother, for whom she now yearned.

'You need to leave,' I said suddenly. 'Get away from him. Go somewhere.'

She looked at me astonished. 'But where, Dr Barrie? Where I can go? No place I can just go.'

I knew she was right but there *had* to be an answer. I remembered hearing some time ago of an Asian women's refuge in Kingston and I managed to track down their number from my friendly contact at the mosque. The advantage of being a GP is that your patients come from all walks of life and I'm just as likely to have an imam as a pandit. The woman at the refuge was helpful but guarded.

'We don't give out our address to men,' she said flatly. 'I understand what you're saying, but if this girl – what's her name? Ayesha? – is in so much trouble she should contact us directly. We'll arrange to meet her, at her home if necessary, and help her pack a few belongings. She is welcome at any time. Our door is always open, well locked, if you see what I mean.' She gave a small laugh.

'But she *can't* ring you,' I protested. 'I've told you already that she hasn't got access to a telephone. I've told her she can use the surgery phone at any time but she's petrified. Scared out of her wits.'

'Yes I can see that, doctor. But I'm afraid I can't say where we are. I have women fleeing abusive husbands and girls escaping the threat of an arranged marriage. For their sake our location is secret.'

I visited Ayesha the next day with Jill, and together we tried to persuade the young mother to return with us to the surgery and telephone the refuge.

'I can't,' she said finally. 'My husband, he know I'm not happy. He says when I run away he will do bad thing.'

'What kind of thing?' asked Jill softly.

'This,' said Ayesha, lifting her sari blouse. Across her chest was a deep scald, between her breasts, and covered by a scab of crusted blood. Before I had a chance to ask how this had happened, Ayesha told Jill how she had gone to the neighbour who lives in the opposite flat to telephone her parents. 'I love my mother so much. I want to tell how I love her,' she sobbed. 'But my husband come home from work and find me there. He says thank you to neighbour and then we go inside. Then he put spoon from hot dhal here,' she said, pointing to her now-covered burn.

Much of what I hear in general practice is based loosely on fact. A smaller amount is pure fiction. There are those who invent symptoms in order that they may qualify for welfare pay-outs; those who exaggerate their tale of woe to earn sympathy; and those who ask me to sign them off for a fortnight to allow their piles 'time to settle, doc' when only that morning you gave his girlfriend her travel vaccinations for *their* holiday in a far away place. Julian Bihari, my ENT consultant uncle, always used to say that sixty per cent of the deaf people referred to him *thought* they were deaf in the hope they could inflate their claim against their employer for noise-induced deafness compensation. The funny thing is, Julian would remark, that after a while they began to believe their own deceit.

185

They would choose to wear a hearing aid in the mistaken belief they really were deaf.

And so with Ayesha I began to have my doubts. She would come to the surgery every week or two, and tell her tale of pitiful neglect and misery. I became sceptical: maybe it really was a tale, one devoid of truth. After all, her husband seemed a pleasant chap in a quiet sort of way. And despite my health visitor's (and my own) encouragement to call the Asian women's refuge, she had consistently refused. No, she would say, I must not. My husband will find me and hurt me.

But then something happened which dispelled my doubts. She stopped coming. Six weeks passed when I had neither sight nor sound of her. Jill, as ever on the case, went to her flat but, predictably, there was no one at home. The lady in the flat across the landing said that Ayesha and Rijul had gone away, adding that she thought that Ayesha's husband continued to live there.

I hoped that they had gone to the refuge. I checked – they had not. I became worried and, after much soul-searching, telephoned the local police station. An officer was duly sent but he, too, met with little success.

'They weren't happy here, you see,' Rijul's father explained to the police sergeant and separately to me when I visited a couple of weeks later. 'They've gone,' he said. 'Don't know where. I'm very upset, left behind on my own.'

The whole thing was very odd. Ayesha and her son seemed to have vanished without trace. Was she and Rijul safe, or had they been hidden away somewhere? Had another, more terrible, fate befallen this mother and child?

I have not seen Rijul, the innocent one, or his mother again.

18

Oppression makes the wise man mad.

Browning 1812–89

The majority of my fellow GPs are unhappy with their lot. Beset by guidelines and constrained by costs, doctors no longer feel in control of their destiny. The job for which they have trained has changed, with the result that many want to quit the profession altogether. I am one of the lucky ones or, put another way, I've made sure that I do not come unstuck by virtue of my inaction. I enjoy general practice but at the same time I see the potential for disillusionment and burn-out.

Sir George Alberti, a recent President of the Royal College of Physicians, has said that 'the old compact between doctors, patients and society' has broken down. How right he is. A 'debate' in 2002 on a medical website revealed many disheartened doctors who posted messages outlining their unhappiness and discontentment. It's not all due to poor pay and a heavy workload. As one author put it: 'It's the change in the psychological compact between the profession, employers, patients and society, so that the job is now different from what doctors expected.' I read a piece in *The Times* at about this time, where the Health Editor summed it up perfectly. 'Doctors', he wrote, 'were once promised a reasonable balance between life and work, autonomy, job security, and deference and respect. Today they face greater accountability, being available to patients for more hours in the day, less autonomy as group-working becomes the norm, evaluation by outsiders and a growing blame culture.'

Sir George said that demanding patients, a litigious culture and greater government involvement had changed the rules in ways that doctors found displeasing. A new compact, he said, needed to be struck. I endorse his words but see difficulties in the practical detail. How can one change people like the oppressive Mrs Blackall, making unreasonable demands left, right and centre? How can one temper the intemperate?

There is a way. Sarath de Alwis Seneviratne, a gynae-cologist with whom I worked at Epsom Hospital, and who has remained a good friend ever since, impressed on me the high value of a patient's belief and expectations. Possessed of endearing charm and wit, the latter never at the expense of anyone else, Sarath taught me far more than obstetric technique.

'No, Michael,' he would urge, seeing that I was becoming impatient with a woman making unreasonable demands and insisting upon unorthodox treatment for her baby to be born in an unconventional manner. 'You're right to say that her birth plan is unsafe but wrong to chastise her.'

'Mrs Edwards,' he would say gently, 'I can see that you've decided to give birth in this way. If that's your wish then so be it. I wouldn't for one moment wish to oppose you. But please,' he would say, taking the woman's hand in his own, 'allow me to go through some of the things that worry me. I'm bothered by aspects of your birth plan. Will you allow me to do this, Mrs Edwards. Please?'

At first I was intolerant of his namby-pamby approach, believing this to be nothing more than an inane attempt to 'suck up' to the patient. But in time I could see that he won them round. Not just some of the time, but all of the time.

'Yes,' agreed Mrs Edwards with a nod of her head, 'I see exactly what you are saying. Thank you. Yes *thank you* for taking so much trouble to explain everything so clearly.'

Sarath would flash a huge smile at the recumbent patient, wink at me and stride out. His brilliance went further, however. With an exceptional intellect (he passed more entrance examinations for Royal College memberships than any other doctor I have known) and a charisma born from clarity of thought, communication and vision, Sarath de Alwis Seneviratne commanded the greatest respect for his surgical acumen. He was a colleague's first choice should they (or their wives) required medical assistance. He must have performed more Caesarean sections on fellow doctors than on any other professional group. He is a gynaecologist who couldn't be more different from Madam Chop Chop.

A few years after entering general practice, I looked after a very different kind of woman from a very different kind of family. Kit was nineteen and the eldest of six children. I knew the family well: Kit's mother was often in my consulting room, weeping as she told of her children's misdemeanours. All six had had trouble at school and I'd had conversations on several occasions with John McGinty, the head teacher at the local secondary school. Kit had been expelled towards the end of her final year at school for possession of cannabis, and her younger siblings were often suspended for their antisocial behaviour. McGinty despaired, as did all of us, but he knew that there was little he or the Social Services could do. The family was dysfunctional and that's all there was to it.

Kit moved in with her boyfriend, and between them they racked up an enormous debt as their drug habit became deeper and more exotic. On three or four occasions I had referred her to the local Addiction Counsellor but each time her partner had mocked her intention to 'go dry' and, feeling foolish in front of his strong character, she had ceased to attend. He had pressurised her into having six of her seven pregnancies aborted, the first one being the result of an earlier relationship, and given that she was just thirteen years of age at the time, a termination seemed a reasonable way out of the situation. By the time she told me that she was again pregnant, she was using vast quantities of cocaine, ecstasy and heroin, whilst her boyfriend abused much of the same, together with copious amount of booze. I think she was quietly pleased when my examination revealed her to be twenty-four weeks' pregnant – too late for it to be terminated.

The pregnancy was complicated by recurrent bladder infections, an episode of pyelonephritis (a kidney infection) and the concern that the baby was small for its corresponding gestational age. This is SFD, or small for dates, and it results from growth retardation of the fetus within the womb; its many causes include maternal smoking, alcoholism and drug addiction.

I knew that Kit would require sensitive handling whilst in labour, not just because of the myriad of medical and obstetric problems but because of her fragile social and domestic situation. My health visitor, Jill, whose remit it is to look after babies and children up to the age of five, did not know the family. There was no reason why she should; after all, Kit's youngest sibling was twelve. So I briefed her on the situation and my involvement with the family to date. Jill visited Kit at home a few weeks before the estimated delivery date and we agreed that a meeting with the Social Services should be convened immediately following the delivery.

It was at once clear to me that Kit would require a special kind of obstetrician – not just a skilled doctor but also someone who would be sensitive to the complexities of the situation, a doctor who would not malign Kit or pass judgement for the life she led, or vilify her partner for the part he had played in perpetuating her problems.

The answer was evident: I would ask Sarath to look after Kit. I telephoned him and outlined her case. Not once did I detect a hint of regret in his voice nor hear a soft sigh of reluctance. He was typically enthusiastic and, reassuringly, was pleased to have been asked.

He sounded just as positive when he called me in the middle of a morning surgery to announce that he had delivered Kit of a baby boy. She was doing OK, he said, but an opiate drip had been set up to stave off an impending heroin withdrawal syndrome. The babe, he continued, was on the special care baby unit for, much as I had feared, he was small for dates. I thought back to the days when I had worked on the very same baby unit and the excitement I had felt when caring for those 'prems' and SFDs, each with its own complex medical needs.

'I suppose you'll be handing Kit over to the psychiatrists now that your job is done?' I said.

'Why?' retorted Sarath.

'Because she'll need to be weaned off her drug habit.'

'Oh,' said Sarath. 'Perhaps. But while she's on my ward, under my care, I'm going to do all I can to help. Michael – it's early days yet.' I could sense his smile down the telephone line.

'Sure. Thanks, Sarath.'

'No worries. I'll see you at the case conference.'

This was a meeting that we had arranged to take place soon after Kit's delivery. It was well-attended. I arrived with Jill, followed by a jolly-looking midwife called Cathy, who told us that she was looking after Kit on the ward upstairs. I looked around the room, which I remembered as one of the outpatient suites within the antenatal clinic, and saw a chap that I recognised as the community drug and alcohol counsellor. We had often discussed mutual patients; and he smiled in acknowledgement of my silent greeting. Jill introduced the social worker, whom I had not met before.

'Shall we make a start?' I said, taking a seat at the large table.

'Oh no, Dr Barrie. Not yet.' The warm Irish voice belonged to the midwife. 'There's a couple more still to come.'

I wasn't sure who else *should* be coming. We had, in my limited experience of case conferences, the usual quorum; I didn't have to deliberate too long, however, for the door suddenly opened and in strode Sarath with, to our disbelief, Kit.

'Good morning, everyone. I am Mr de Alwis Seneviratne, one of the obstetricians and I…' he stopped short as he assimilated the look of surprise on the faces around the table.

'Goodness!' he said with a wide, cheeky grin. 'Never seen a new mum before?' He guided Kit to a chair as he spoke. 'Kit's got every right to be here,' he continued, interpreting our surprise as indignation at her presence. 'After all, this meeting's about her, isn't it?' Kit was nervous and bewildered by the group of people who now stared as Sarath turned towards her.

'Right, my dear?' he said. *My dear?* That's just so like him, I thought. I couldn't have said that without appearing patronising but Sarath pulls it off perfectly, every time bringing round even the most challenging patient to his way of thinking. He has a knack, similar to that of Creamer.

Jill suggested that once Kit's body was rid of heroin she should be allowed home with her baby, whom we learnt had been named Blake. Jill said she would visit daily to make sure that mum and baby were settling in the small, but probably adequate, apartment.

'Her boyfriend still regards the flat as his, but actually it's a council property,' said Jill with a knowing smile. 'I don't think he'll try and push her out.'

'Why would he do that, Kit?' I asked, looking at my patient.

Kit didn't get a chance to respond. 'You don't know what he's like!' cried Cathy. 'He's been on the postnatal wards most afternoons, pissed as a newt when he's not high on dope. Shown no interest in his son and made it quite clear that he's not going to change his ways.'

'Yes, but I see what Michael means,' said Sarath. 'Why would he push her out?'

Jill gave Cathy a telling look and then smiled at Kit.

'Because,' said Jill, 'he relies on Kit's benefit payments to fund his habit.'

Kit was quiet but her face was sad, and I could see that she was preoccupied.

'If she stays clean,' continued Jill, 'as she's promised she will, she'll be using the money to look after Blake. Won't you, Kit?'

Kit nodded.

'My concern is that her partner will become angry, maybe aggressive, when he can't afford his drugs, and he'll push Kit onto the street.' Jill spoke slowly but deliberately. Kit had a real ally in Jill. It was obvious that she was a health visitor who would fight Kit's corner in many a subsequent battle.

The community drug and alcohol counsellor offered to support Kit and suggested that her boyfriend avail himself of professional help.

I saw a lot of Kit and Blake in the months that followed. Her boyfriend's chemical addiction deepened and he spent much of Blake's first year inside gaol as he stole in order to fund his drug habit. I didn't see much of him even when he was out of prison. His presence was overbearing and, like du Maurier's Svengali, he was forever trying to wield his sinister powers over the weaker members of my primary health care team.

He disappeared from his infant child's life when Blake was fourteen months, and what had once been a dysfunctional family now became one of the country's many single-parent families.

Kit struggled financially, it must be said, but I can only praise her devotion and love for her child. Blake is, in fact, only a few days older than my younger child, Alex, and I think his mother's plight heightened my awareness not just of a child's needs but also their unique vulnerability.

A child is all that is best about us. The great writer Amanda Craig described a child's beauty, energy, curiosity and creativity, and their overwhelming need to give and receive love, which are indeed the things we value most in ourselves. She said that children are what redeem us as flawed and ageing individuals, for they give us a glimpse of our own perfectibility. They are our own arrows into the future, and are irreplaceable with their unique character and destiny.

I had, at about this time, a young woman patient whom I will call Ruth. She was twenty-five, attractive and intelligent. She had graduated a couple of years earlier from the London School of Economics, and now worked for a large investment house in the City. I saw Ruth a couple of times each year when she attended for routine contraceptive checks, but one day she came to see me about an entirely different problem.

Ruth had found a lump in her breast whilst in the shower a day or so earlier. There was indeed a small, discrete cyst in the upper, outer quadrant of her left breast and I was sure that this was innocuous. A benign fibro-adenoma, I said, explaining that it is known as a breast mouse because it scuttles away from the examining fingers. Quite benign, I remember telling her as I dictated a letter to our excellent breast surgeon, but best removed just to be sure.

The surgeon and I were astonished when the histology came back as breast cancer. Ruth was devastated. The most successful outcome in breast cancer treatment has been achieved by 'adjuvant' therapy – therapy applied after an operation to remove the growth, in order to suppress secondary tumour formation. In breast cancer this takes the form of radiotherapy and chemotherapy. But Ruth wasn't having any of it.

The surgeon, himself trained by Eric Finch at St Thomas's, couldn't understand her reticence. He reckoned that he knew what was best for his patients and couldn't be dealing with someone who thought otherwise. But with Ruth it wasn't like that: she had thought very long and very hard about the treatment modalities being offered, and had chosen to decline adjuvant therapy. The surgical team pushed Ruth back in my direction with the insinuation that I knock some sense into her. Perhaps I misinterpreted the thrust of the consultant's actual wording but I felt the onus had been put on me to 'make her see sense'.

I spent much time with Ruth in the weeks that followed, counselling her about radiotherapy: what it would involve, the side effects, the ways in which it kills cancer cells, and the proven track record it has in promoting a patient's remission. I did the same for chemotherapy, which in breast cancer treatment takes the form of hormonal therapy. I explained that her surgeon had removed the cancer, but the 'microinvasive' theory assumes that cancer cells break off from the main tumour mass and drift to other areas of the body, both near and far. Thus it is possible in breast cancer, for example, for malignant cells to have already spread around the body long before the woman even discovers a lump in her breast. An operation to remove the lump, no matter how much of the breast is removed, will leave behind the cancer seeding itself in distant sites. Adjuvant therapy, especially hormonal chemotherapy, will destroy those cells wherever they happen to lurk.

Ruth was an educated and willing listener. Not once

did she argue with the scientific facts that I presented and nor was she ever cussed or remonstrative. Amidst the strain of fraught consultations with my many demanding patients, and the tension of trying to sort out Kit's calamitous social problems, I found the consultations with Ruth to be a welcome opportunity to debate a patient's critical dilemmas on an equal intellectual level.

Ruth accepted that her chances of survival were greatest with post-operative radiotherapy and hormonal manipulation: she had ample enough foresight to respect evidence-based clinical practice. But she took the view that the surgeon had removed the tumour from her breast and that if cancerous cells were left behind, then so be it.

She would take her chances.

Kit, meanwhile, was enjoying motherhood although it was far from plain sailing. She had applied to the housing officer at the council to be rehoused. Her partner had returned to prison for the third time in so many months, and she felt threatened by his demands for money. Kit was dry as far as drugs were concerned but her wayward partner exerted a continual pressure on her to lead a depraved life such as his. He brought back drug pushers to the flat, and Jill reported her concerns to Social Services, who at last agreed that the only way to safeguard little Blake without resorting to a care order would be to rehouse Kit at a secret location. Her new council accommodation was just a few streets away from the first flat but she was quite safe from Blake's father: he would have been too inebriated to have been able to harm her, and in any event he returned to prison just a few weeks later.

One morning in March 2000, I received a letter from Ruth's mother. She wasn't my patient, indeed I'd never met her, but she seemed to know of her daughter's diagnosis and my care of her. Her letter criticised me for not doing enough to encourage her daughter to pursue what she termed the 'correct and acceptable' treatment for breast cancer. She berated me for the innumerable consultations I had had with Ruth, each time failing to convince her daughter of the unmistakable benefits of life-saving treatment. She used to be a nurse, she wrote, and was disturbed by my most unorthodox treatment.

I was livid. I could understand that her anger was more likely a reflection of the grief she was suffering, knowing that her daughter was not receiving the 'pull out all the stops' treatment, but she just didn't know the facts of the case. It put me in a difficult position: I could not respond to her criticisms without breaching my duty of confidentiality, but equally I did not want to inflame what I imagined might already be a rather fraught mother–daughter bond by telling my patient that her mother had sent me a terse letter.

What to do? I tried to imagine what Creamer would have done. Or Sarath. Even Finch. In the end I wrote a short note to Ruth's mother saying that I could not discuss her daughter's case without Ruth's written permission. Her mother was furious! She wrote another letter, this time far more vitriolic, and accused me of clinical negligence. I passed a copy to my solicitor and upon his suggestion showed it to Ruth when she next attended the surgery.

Ruth was upset that her mother should have taken this stance. She affirmed that her wish to decline anti-cancer treatment was hers alone, and that as her doctor I could not have done more to try to change that decision. My intuition that Ruth's relationship with her mother was precarious had been correct, and Ruth was adamant that I should be allowed the opportunity to defend the criticisms levelled at me, which she felt were hurtful and unfair. She signed a note of authorisation granting consent for me to discuss her clinical details.

In my letter to her mother I presented the facts in a

straightforward way. My letter, as I had expected, generated yet more correspondence from the vexatious woman and in the end I thought it best to let the matter be, leaving her last couple of letters unanswered.

Kit and Ruth occupied a great deal more of my time than the two and half thousand or so other patients on my list, but every minute of this was an education for me and I hope of value to them too.

Blake had his second birthday and his mother became pregnant by her new partner. An ultrasound scan showed she was carrying twins. My smiling congratulations belied my inner groan of despair as I forecast a troubled horizon for the hapless woman.

I maintained an excellent doctor–patient relationship with Ruth right up until her death eighteen months later. She had developed disseminated malignant disease and the terminal stages of her young life were both inexorable and unbearable, despite her unwavering fortitude. She was aged twenty-seven.

19

Cyprus 2002 and the spoken word strikes a discordant note.

'*Oi! Wez Powel?*'

'*Eez in da powerl.*'

'*An Maaahl-cam? Wez 'im gottoo den? Eh?*'

'*Plying powerl.*'

'*Ow.*'

'*Woi d'ya wunner know? Eh?*'

'*Aw, nuffink. Juz wunner-in.*'

What is it about holiday resorts? Wherever one goes, it is an inevitable fact that one's fellow countrymen are, and I make an apology here if what follows sounds a trifle snobbish, terribly common. No matter where on the globe one visits, nor the cost of the accommodation once there, the 'Brits' are there; in force. The Brit who will say *Powel* for Paul, and *powerl* for pool. The Brits who 'abitually drop their h's and make incredible admissions of guilt by their use of double negatives. The Brits whose faces are creased by the furrows inflicted by years of smoking; the same vice which is responsible for the phlegmy cackle which rattles inexorably in the terminal phases of their laughter.

Ha ha ha ha, hee hee hee hee, ha ha ha ha, hee hee hee hee, rattle rattle rattle, splutter, rattle, splutter...

Who am I to criticise? I − the doctor who respects human life in all its forms; the physician healing irrespective of race, colour and class. Class? What an enigma!

One talks of upper, middle and lower class just as I might talk of the three segments of the oesophagus. But the middle part of the gullet is *always* in the middle. From birth 'til death its site, and therefore its title, remains unchanged. And a title or name it is: nothing more, old sport! But is it fair that mankind has bestowed upon the humble oesophagus a classification? We apply labels to matter, both animate and inanimate, and in so doing cause hurt and resentment.

Simon Atkinson, of MORI, conducted a poll in 2002 and found that two-thirds of Britons regarded themselves as working-class, one in ten more than had in 1997. His researchers were puzzled by the remarkable rekindling in proletarian solidarity at a time when numbers of working-class people were declining. But we can all name working-class heroes like David Beckham, Atkinson said, and when you think of them you relate to positive working-class values such as honesty, hard work and a strong feeling of community. I agree.

The Oxford-educated lawyer who, like his father and *his* father before him, is called to the Bar is, unarguably, middle-class. But what of his son who flunks his A-levels and becomes a road sweeper? Is he lower-class by virtue of his employment? Or middle-class because of his parents' 'membership'? And what about his fellow road sweeper who attends night school and then law school and ultimately takes silk?

Robert and Alex are playing in the 'powerl' and I'm chatting to a fellow Brit. It's both hot and humid and we're sticking to small talk. Fred's a roofer; a bit older than I, and here with his family. When Fred left school he drifted around before finding work as a hod carrier with a local builder. His father, he says, was a milkman but he himself didn't fancy getting out of bed at the crack of dawn for the rest of his life, so he stuck with the building trade, eventually setting himself up as a one-man band or, as he put it, Jack of all things 'constructibble'.

Now he owns a small construction outlet and employs a manager and nine operatives. Fred is well-off: he owns a holiday cottage in Tuscany and a yacht currently moored somewhere off the south of France. His two daughters attend a private school. He's a nice chap and we get on well. So middle or lower-class? I put the question to him.

'Workin'-class,' he says emphatically, 'and proud of it. Always will be proud of it.'

His eldest daughter, a rather serious girl, has been following our chatter. When she hears that I am a doctor, she says that she too hopes to become a doctor.

'I know it's a bit early to say, but I hope to be an orthopaedic surgeon.'

'That's great...' I begin.

'An' she'll be workin'-class an' all,' her father interrupts with a smile.

I nod but am unconvinced. Somehow I cannot envisage Fred's daughter — educated, say, at Roedean then Bart's — becoming one of the country's top bone specialists and all the while remaining a working-class lass. I don't think so.

Take me, for instance. My father was educated at an ordinary state-funded school, and his family had little in the way of money. His upbringing was very much 'working-class'. His academic studies were rewarded by a consultant's post at Charing Cross Hospital, one of the capital's leading teaching hospitals. He had an unrivalled reputation, with his research into neonatal resuscitation published in the world's medical press, and throughout his professional life was much in demand both in the National

Health and private sectors. My privileges are inherited but my livelihood earned. So what does that make me?

Does it matter? *Should it matter?*

My paternal grandmother, Ida, when asked for her religion or, more rudely, her social class, would invariably answer: 'I'm a person.' Such humanistic ideology nurtures a tolerant, if somewhat uncritical, personality; better that, she would say, than judge others by their class or religion or, worse, perceived social status.

In the opening lines of the *The Great Gatsby*, F. Scott Fitzgerald wrote: 'Whenever you feel like criticizing anyone, just remember that all the people in this world haven't had the advantages that you've had.' And so my father's mother, Ida – humanist and Pole – instilled in me much of the same thinking. She was born in 1898 in Lwów (then Lemberg, for a while Lvov, now L'viv), capital of the Polish Ukraine, to David and Gitta Weingarten.

Lemberg was at that time part of the Austro-Hungarian Empire, which encompassed not just Austria and Hungary, but also territory that became Czechoslovakia as well as parts of Poland, the Ukraine, Romania, Yugoslavia and Italy. The provincial villages of this vast empire comprised poor yet self-sufficient farming communities, and Czernica was no exception.

David and Gitta had four other children besides Ida.

Their first child, Sophia, died at the age of three. Then came Nathan, followed by Ida, then another girl, Ninette, and finally a son in 1907 whom they named Ignaz. Ida never knew Sophia – her death was three years prior to Ida's birth – and so it was to Ninette, her younger sister, that my grandmother grew especially close. While Ignaz and Nathan would help on their father's farm, she and Ninette would fondly talk of their aspirations, the six-year age difference between Ida and Ninette seemingly having little impact on the sisters' friendship.

Ida met my grandfather, Emil Bihari, during the First World War. He was Hungarian and so called upon to fight in Emperor Franz Joseph's battle to save the empire from collapse. Emil was born in 1897, one year earlier than Ida, to Gyula and Ilona Blau. When Emil was aged three years, and his brother Max just two, their father, Gyula, was knocked down and killed by a horse-drawn cart laden with beer kegs. The two boys never got over the sudden death of their father but their life was to be made more miserable still by their mother's remarriage to a cussed and alcoholic tyrant. In an attempt to establish his own identity, young Emil assumed the Hungarian surname of 'Bihari'.

Emil Blau, or Emil Bihari as he now was, had known Ida for only a few months when his battalion was ordered east. Emil promised his Polish sweetheart that he would come back to wed her; two years elapsed and Ida must have doubted that the haughty Hungarian would ever return. But return he did and my grandmother would recount the tale of when she was milking the cows and, struggling across the farmyard with a full pail of milk, was startled by a heavy-booted step behind her. 'I turned,' she would say, 'and there was Emil, handsome and resplendent in his uniform, beaming from ear to ear. I was so shocked that I let go of the bucket and spilt the milk all over his trousers and boots.'

They were married a few months later and, with the war now over and the Austro-Hungarian Empire dismembered, Emil returned home to Budapest with his bride. His evil stepfather was dead, so he and Ida moved in with Ilona and brother Max. Ida found the early years of marriage difficult: whilst her family joined the other inhabitants of Czernica in their proud celebration of being once again Polish, she struggled in a foreign land still in turmoil from the death of its Emperor and its defeat in war. Moreover, and far worse, she could not speak Hungarian and Emil was not familiar with Polish. Both were Jews but not conversant with Yiddish. How she must have yearned for little Czernica.

In due course Emil Bihari took on work as an engineer,

later relocating with the firm to Berlin. In 1925, Ida gave birth to their first child, Gyula, followed two years later by the birth of their second son, my father Herbert. They had a comfortable apartment in the Niederschöneweide district of Berlin, enjoying the friendship of fellow Berliners, and Gyula and Herbert commenced their schooling at the *Volksschule* in Karlshorst.

The Biharis' cosy existence was soon to be threatened, however. At the end of January 1933, Adolf Hitler, a political outsider who headed a small, discredited band on the lunatic fringe of political life, became Chancellor of a coalition government with the right-wing Nationalist Party. A month later the Reichstag building caught fire; Hitler blamed the Communists, and the President, von Hindenburg, was persuaded to suspend individual and civil liberties, and to grant legislative power to the Chancellor by a two-thirds majority of those present and voting. The Nazis gained a mere 44 per cent of the vote, but when the Reichstag reconvened in March that year, an act was passed that gave dictatorial powers to Hitler. A ballot was held, but this time all the Communists (and some of the Social Democrats) were prevented from attending, thereby ensuring that Hitler won by a majority vote to become Führer of Germany.

A few days later, on April 1st, the Nazis initiated a

boycott of Jewish businesses and shops across Germany. Soldiers were stationed in front of Jewish-owned stores and the Star of David was painted on countless doors to indicate a Jewish business or household. People with the most tenuous links to the Jewish faith were dismissed from their jobs and new laws deposed Jews and political opponents from teaching and governmental offices. Jews lost their academic titles. Textbooks portraying Jews as monsters were widely distributed to schools and colleges. At break-time in my father's school, children played the game *Jews Out!*

One month on, in May, thousands of Nazi students stormed universities, libraries and bookshops in thirty cities and destroyed 'un-German' books in huge bonfires with the aim of 'purifying' German culture. In the same month, Hitler dissolved the political parties in opposition so that by July his party was the sole political force with himself as undisputed leader. The official persecution of the Jews had begun.

My grandfather remained optimistic that the morals and sensibilities of the German people would prevail: encouraged by the genuine warmth and hospitality of his non-Jewish friends and work colleagues, he was relieved when the boycott of April 1933 was prematurely terminated. His optimism was shortlived: the Nuremberg

Race Laws, in 1935, stripped him and his family of citizenship in the Reich.

Emil had Hungarian nationality, but for him the Nuremberg Laws had far worse consequences: his life in Berlin became restricted as, for the first time in history, Jews were now to be persecuted not for their religious beliefs but for their racial origin.

My father, then aged eight, remembers the effect of the Nuremberg Laws. He recalls signs saying *Juden unerwünscht* (Jews unwelcome) on the doors of shops, theatres, restaurants and hotels. He had his hair cut in a shop displaying such a sign, and the barber deliberately scratched the back of his neck with sharp scissors. He learned to play the violin at the Konservatorium der Musik von Richard Paul, in Johannisthal, but the journey there and back was becoming hazardous on account of threats and harassment. But worse was to come.

Ida visited the butcher one day to buy meat, only to find that he had 'disappeared'; then the grocer's shop in Niederschöneweide shut, with talk that he had been 'taken away'; a teacher at the boys' school vanished mid-term. There were rumours that they had been taken away for 're-education', but all had in common just one thing: they were Jews.

One evening in the autumn of 1937, Emil decided to

visit the doctor, a family friend, with the intention of inviting him to spend an evening with Ida, himself and the boys. He shared Emil's abhorrence of Hitler's government, and the two men would often discuss politics late into the night. The doctor's house-keeper was usually indifferent to those she met, being neither friendly nor unfriendly to them, but she was truculent to the man who now asked if the 'Herr Doktor' was at home. She told Emil that her employer had gone away and would not be returning. My grandfather would later recount how the woman's denial of his friend's whereabouts, and her hostility, forced him to the unwelcome realisation that the wave of antisemitism sweeping across Germany had made it unsafe for his family to stay. Emil Bihari and his family were Jews: they had to get out.

A fortnight later, in November 1937, he travelled alone to Britain in search of work; unless he was employed, the Home Office would not authorise the requisite visas allowing his wife and sons to join him. He searched frantically for a job, indeed any job, but his difficulties with the language (he was fluent in German and Hungarian, but could not speak English) were a major obstacle. The Home Office had granted him a four-week visa and so he pleaded with officials at their bureau in Piccadilly Place for an extension.

After six desperate months he struck lucky: Bryce Ltd, an engineering works at Hackbridge in Surrey, gave him employment. Bryce's supervisor wrote to the Home Office, who replied by return:

> The Under Secretary of State is directed to refer to the application to the Ministry of Labour from Bryce Ltd. ... to say that it has been decided to vary the condition on which Mr. Emil Bihari was given leave to land in the United Kingdom so as to permit of his employment and so as to postpone the date on or before which he is required to leave this country until the 30th November, 1938. His passport should be forwarded, in the enclosed envelope, to this Department for the necessary endorsement.

Emil returned to Germany to collect what to him mattered more than anything: his family. They left the country discreetly, without furniture and with just a few belongings. Documents were thrown into an attaché case and included Herbert's *Volksschule* reports. Children's termly reports must be signed by their father; Herbert's had been signed by Emil, except for the winter term report of 1937 – on this Ida forged his signature although not with much authenticity! In Britain they rented a flat in Wynash Gardens, Carshalton, a suburb of London sounding uncannily similar to Karlshorst, the city suburb where the boys had gone to school.

The family's escape was both timely and in time; in November 1938 anti-Jewish violence erupted throughout the Reich. *Kristallnacht* was the precipitant in the destruction of Jewish existence in Germany: one thousand synagogues were burned, seven thousand Jewish businesses were ruined, ninety-six Jews were killed, and Jewish hospitals and homes were destroyed. Thirty thousand Jews were arrested, and deported to the concentration camps of Dachau, Buchenwald and Sachsenhausen. In Berlin, thousands more were expelled from their homes. And in Niederschöneweide, as elsewhere in Nazi-Germany, Torah scrolls and sacred books were burned on immense bonfires and Jewish-owned property was confiscated.

Six days after *Kristallnacht* ('Crystal Night', so called because of the shattering of glass from Jewish-owned shops), Jews were barred from attending school and within a month Jews were denied access to public places. Panic reigned as Jews tried to flee, but in less than a year Germany was at war and her borders closed. For those left behind it was just too late.

20

'Gee-us a fag!'

'Nah. S'mer larst wunn.'

'Agh! Shah-yer fise, stewpid giht.'

The hot Cyprian climate, infused with sporadic warm breezes from the Mediterranean, offers itself as a milieu for the hollers and whoops and shouts. I am reminded of the narrator's words in Fitzgerald's *The Great Gatsby*: 'I was within and without, simultaneously enchanted and repelled by the inexhaustible variety of life.'

Alex turned three last week; he is splashing Robert who, two years his elder, is exacting his revenge with a lethal-looking water pistol. Their laughter is lost in the cacophony of happy shrieks.

Neither they – nor I – would be here today if it were not for the foresightedness of their great-grandfather. His family, of which I am so proud to be a part, are the lucky ones: to him I am thankful.

★　★　★

At the end of the war, my grandparents contacted the Red Cross to inquire what had become of their respective families in Hungary and Poland. Ida knew that the Jews in Germany had perished but she feared for those in distant locations such as Poland and the Ukraine. When she left Czernica in 1923, five years after the end of the First World War and with the once-mighty Austro-Hungarian Empire now shattered, Poland had established herself as an independent republic. During these high-spirited years of nationalist vitality, Ignaz had waded into a river to catch fish and he had trodden on a rusty nail. News of his death from tetanus reached Ida in Berlin via Nathan, who was by this time married. How Ida must have longed to see her brother, and Ninette, her dearest sister.

Polish independence was shortlived: Poland was invaded by Germany in 1939, resulting in Chamberlain's famous declaration of war, and was absorbed into the Nazi Reich. The Germans were methodical and systematic in ensuring that all Jews within its borders were exterminated and the chances of the Red Cross office in London finding news that Ida's family were safe, say, in America or even Britain were indeed slim. Eventually the Red Cross received a response to their enquiries and the grim news was passed to Emil and Ida: Emil's mother Ilona and his brother Max, together with Max's wife and their young daughter, had been murdered in Budapest. Under Nazi occupation 136,000 people had died in Lwów's Jewish ghetto and 350,000 more in concentration camps. Ida's parents, David and Gitta, her beloved sister Ninette, and her brother Nathan, together with Nathan's wife and two young daughters, had perished at the hands of their Nazi persecutors. One way or the other, Ida's four siblings had predeceased her, but the hardest loss to bear was the death of her sister.

So what became of Czernica? At the end of the war Poland was liberated from Nazi rule by the Soviet Union's Red Army. But there was a catch: rather than allow the Poles their freedom, Stalin kept Poland for himself; Lwów became Lvov and was incorporated into Soviet Ukraine. The city's inhabitants did not, however, consider themselves Russian and became a displaced population, eventually being forced westwards to the severely depopulated Breslau (now Wrocław), which Russia had confiscated from Germany. Breslau seemed to offer the Poles of Lwów (Lvov to be accurate) and those in her satellite towns and villages, such as Czernica, a ready-made home. The few that remained in Lvov were subjected to a brutally repressive rule from Moscow. But my grandmother's lovely family were not alive at the time these post-war acts were committed.

Soviet Ukraine severed its ties with Moscow in 1991 and Lvov assumed her Ukranian, and latest, name: L'viv.

To be alive is a wonderful thing. The happiness of the children here in Cyprus is testimony to the need for tolerance of, and respect for, all mankind. Brian Creamer and Sarath de Alwis Seneviratne, both kind and benevolent men, had taught me that; so too had Eric Finch who, despite his armour of steel, possessed an innate humanity. Finch had many faults inherent in his arrogance but I don't think he was stuck up, or even stuffy.

What a great word! *Stuffy* – the allusion to the stuffed shirt displayed by a dummy in a shop window, suggesting a pompous and vacuous person. *The figure is not only pompous-looking but hollow*. Who said that?

The Biharis realised that whilst the British were a tolerant people, there was no place for self-pity; Emil, like many of his generation, assumed the rôle of head of his household and insisted that his family adapt if they wanted acceptance within, rather than *without*, the culture of their latest 'host' country.

He forbade from the outset the use of their common

tongue – German. If someone has something to say, he would insist, then say it in English! Don't know the words? Then mime it. For his two boys, aged twelve and ten, this was no mean feat but ultimately it provided them with an invaluable gift: a love for grammatically correct usage of the English language, both spoken and written.

I think the prohibition by immigrant parents of the use of their mother tongue was commonplace amongst families seeking refuge in war-time Britain. A correspondent to *The Times* in 2002 wrote:

On arrival I spoke only German and my parents spoke Hungarian, but deliberately only spoke English to me as they wanted me to speak [English] without an accent. They succeeded and I accepted the situation of the dual languages. I shall always be grateful to them for their foresight in so admirably equipping me for my life in this country.

Gyula, who by now had chosen to call himself Julian, won a place to read medicine at University College Hospital; he was followed two years later by Herbert. Julian completed his ENT training in London but on a visit to Wales in the 1950s realised that this was where he wished to settle. He was appointed consultant in ear, nose and throat surgery at Singleton Hospital in Swansea.

When I was walking with Uncle Julian and my father along the cliff-top path on the Gower Peninsula, I asked whether either of them had allowed time for reflection on the years spent in Germany.

'Allowed?' my father said, surprised by my choice of word. 'Why should I have to *allow* myself to think of the past?'

Julian knew what I was getting at. It used to be said that aspiring offspring of immigrant parents lack spontaneity lest they expose something of their humble or peasant origin. Tony Tanner, Fellow of King's College, Cambridge, termed it 'sloughing off' the immigrant identity.

'What Michael means,' Julian said, 'is whether we are *conscious* of our life before coming to Britain.'

'I don't think about it,' my father replied. The path was less steep now. To our right was Bracelet Bay and I squinted my eyes at the coruscation of sunlight on the neat folds made by the small waves.

'That's exactly what Michael meant,' Julian continued. 'We don't allow ourselves to think back that far. So much has happened since, but we shouldn't deny it either.'

'Of course not,' my father had agreed. Julian had stopped and I could see that he was looking at the twin islets off the end of Mumbles Head. He had once told me that the name Mumbles derives from *mamelles* (in French meaning breasts), which is thought to refer to the two small bony mounds that now were just ahead of us.

My father had changed his name in his final year at University College Hospital Medical School and it was as Herbert Barrie that he qualified in 1950. Julian had qualified two years earlier – as Dr Bihari.

'And d'you regret not keeping our father's name?' Julian asked suddenly. 'After all, Papa was so proud of his Hungarian roots. We all knew that!'

Julian and I turned expectantly to my father but he did not answer; or if he did, the words were inaudible over the cries of the gulls circling in their hundreds high above the Bristol Channel.

On a chilly February morning in 1976, Emil Bihari drove his wife to a doctor's appointment at Charing Cross Hospital. She had a mild skin disorder and Herbert had asked one of his dermatological colleagues to take a look at her. Emil dropped Ida off at the hospital's main entrance and then went to find a parking place.

A quarter of an hour or so later, a hospital porter walking along Fulham Palace Road saw, a little way ahead, an elderly, besuited gentleman supporting his frame against the railings that skirt the hospital's perimeter. As the porter ran to his aid he saw that the old man was struggling to breathe.

A few minutes later my grandmother thanked the dermatologist for his advice and, clutching her prescription, emerged into the outpatient reception area. She was surprised that her husband was not there but presumed that he'd had difficulty in finding somewhere to park. She ambled over to the information desk in the main foyer; but after waiting for half an hour there still was no sign of him.

'Excuse me.' She addressed the clerk seated behind the high-level Formica counter. 'I don't know where my husband is.'

'His name?' intoned the clerk. Her imperturbable countenance and composed remoteness belied her young age. She's just a girl, my grandmother thought.

'Emil Bihari. He was supposed ...'

'Inpatient or outpatient?' The 'girl' had perfected the art of relaxing all of her facial muscles so that the skin and soft tissue overlying them were devoid of expression. Her question, in the event, went unanswered for at that moment, and surely by a stroke of coincidence, my mother — at that time a consultant microbiologist at

Charing Cross Hospital – happened to stride across the foyer. Ida spotted her daughter-in-law instantly amongst the white-coated clutch of doctors. It's that strange phenomenon whereby a familiar face can jump out from amongst a thousand strange ones.

'Dinah!' she cried. 'I'm so worried, so very worried…'

I was then a seven-year-old, and I recall little of my grandfather's death. He had been resuscitated in the A&E department at Charing Cross, but his heart was failing and it gave up a few days later.

I do remember, on the other hand, my excitement as a young boy accompanying my father as, on foot, we crisscrossed the narrow Fulham streets in search of where my grandfather had parked his car for the last time.

21

Mr Lodworski may have been eighty-three years of age but he had led an active life. Tennis and golf were his favourite pastimes, and often he could be seen pootling around the town on his bicycle. He came in every few months to have his blood pressure checked and we would talk about this and that. He had come to Britain in the 1930s to escape the rise of antisemitism in Eastern Europe; in this way his plight – in fact his whole persona – was akin to that of my grandfather. I have but hazy memories of Emil, and much of it, lamentably, has been surplanted by old Lodworski: when I try to picture Emil's face, my mind sees only Mr Lodworski.

One day Lodworski presented himself at my surgery with a cough. I listened to his chest, diagnosed infective bronchitis and gave him some antibiotics. For a while he improved but a fortnight later he was back to say that he had twice coughed up some blood. I arranged for him to have a chest X-ray that afternoon, and with astonishing efficiency the radiologist faxed the result the next morning. Mr Lodworski had lung cancer.

I referred him to our local chest physician because good

medical practice dictates that this is what a GP should do, but I knew that Lodworski's days were numbered. Cancer can be 'treated' by one of three ways: cutting it out (surgery); destroying it by irradiation (radiotherapy); or killing the mitotic cells with powerful drugs (cytotoxic chemotherapy). A combination of these methods is generally employed and often newly published research tools are tried – such as monoclonal antibodies or gene therapy. Occasionally the tumour is so extensive, or resistant to treatment, that none are used.

Patients with lung cancer – properly *bronchial carcinoma* – fare badly. I see around two or three new cases each year: most are dead within six months of diagnosis. I have two remarkable patients, a man and a woman, who are alive ten and thirteen years respectively from the date of their diagnosis. But therein lies the reason for their successful outcomes. Both had chest X-rays performed for reasons other than suspected lung cancer.

The man was the director of a City firm where all senior employees enjoyed the privilege of a yearly executive health screen: blood tests, electrocardiogram, audiogram, chest X-ray and so on. He didn't have any symptoms attributable to his chest; indeed, there was no clinical reason to perform the X-ray, which showed a small mass in the left lower lobe of his lung.

The woman had had an even luckier escape. Having had too much to drink at her niece's hen party, some clever arse had had the bright idea of seeing how high each could toss a peanut before catching it – openmouthed. The nut shot straight into her right main bronchus and, amidst much choking and spluttering, she was taken by ambulance to hospital. There a chest X-ray revealed not only the tell-tale signs of an inhaled foreign body but also a suspicious-looking shadow within her left lung field. The casualty officer's diagnosis was confirmed the next day by fibre-optic bronchoscopy.

With early diagnosis comes the real possibility of cure. My two 'survivors' had their tumours removed surgically before spread had occurred. It would have taken several months before the cancer had grown large enough to cause a cough with blood-stained sputum or breathlessness, and by then it would have been too late.

I could sense that Mr Lodworski, who sat now at my desk, already knew the reason for his bloody phlegm. His expression was gentle, almost acquiescent, as I began the difficult task of explaining the jargon-filled fax before me.

'Mr Lodworski,' I began. 'How long have you been coughing for?'

'Ah, doctor,' he replied wisely, 'you know it's been just a few weeks.'

'Six, would you say? Longer?'

The old man's soft eyes were gazing through the window behind me. 'Well, what's a couple of months when you've got a bit of a cough, eh?' He glanced in my direction then back at the view outside, before adding, 'Perhaps three months.'

'And how long have you been smoking?' I asked. My tone was not remonstrative.

'Long enough for this to be cancer,' said Lodworski quietly, his eyebrows raised yieldingly towards me.

Mr Lodworski, never one to complain, remained stoical throughout his short illness. He allowed me to organise visits from my district nurse and support from the Macmillan team and, more practically, adaptations to be made to his narrow Victorian three-storey house. He was determined to die gracefully.

But Lodworski had a son and a daughter who were angry; angry that their father's diagnosis had not been made earlier. His life, they said, could have been saved if his cancer had been detected sooner; angry that he was not receiving sufficient input from my primary health care team; and angry that their father – who had come from Poland to enlist in the RAF, where he served His Majesty's war-torn country – was dying, neglected by an uncaring and indifferent NHS which they felt was failing him at his hour of need.

But it wasn't true. None of it. His diagnosis could not possibly have been made any earlier and even if it had, the histology showed his tumour to be so aggressive that there could never have been any hope of a cure. Most galling of all was his son and daughter's perception that I was not doing enough. I do not ever seek praise or recognition for the care I deliver, but it disquietens me to know that the standard of this care is being questioned.

One evening my receptionist buzzed me to say that Mr Lodworski's daughter had arrived at the practice and demanded that she be seen.

'I did tell her that you were busy,' explained the receptionist, 'but she is most insistent.'

I don't normally see someone who just turns up without an appointment but I made an exception for Mr Lodworski's daughter. Her father was dying and I reckoned that her family's criticism of me was a manifestation of the tremendous grief that doubtless they were enduring.

She stormed into the consulting room and it was fortuitous for us both that I was not examining a patient.

'Doctor, you need to visit my father this evening!' she barked.

'I'm happy to help, by all means. What is the matter with him?' I inquired.

'I don't want to go into that now. Just visit.'

231

'Please, Miss Lodworski, give me an indication. It would help me to decide whether I need to bring any special equipment or medication.' I tried to sound reasonable.

'What is it with you doctors? Questions, questions, questions,' sighed the woman impatiently. Streuth, was hers a contrast to the benevolent character of her father. Perhaps her prescriptive and proscriptive approach was what Tanner meant by 'sloughing off your immigrant identity'; the air had become tense.

'I…' I began.

'If I say you will visit, then you'll visit,' interrupted Miss Lodworski.

'I think it best,' I said gently, 'if I telephone your father to see what the matter is. If he should want me to visit then I shall go and see him.'

'He will say he doesn't want a visit,' she snapped.

'In which case I won't go,' I said. 'It is, after all, up to him.'

'Listen! If I say you must visit,' the old man's daughter repeated, 'you will visit.'

I showed her to the door and continued my evening surgery. I called Mr Lodworski later that evening.

'Ah, Dr Barrie!' he exclaimed. 'How good to hear your voice on this blustery evening. How can I help?'

'Help?' I said. 'I'm supposed to be helping you. Your daughter has suggested I contact you. Something was troubling her.'

'What is?' His voice on the telephone line was clear and bright.

'Don't know. That's why I'm calling.'

'I wouldn't worry, doctor. You know what daughters are like. She's always fretting about something. Says I don't eat enough. Complains I drink too much whisky. Moans that I smoke—' He paused. 'Still.'

'You smoke as much as you want, Mr Lodworski,' I smiled invisibly into the telephone but he sensed the amusement in my voice and we both laughed.

'Thank you, doctor,' said Lodworski.

'Goodnight.'

'Goodnight, doctor.'

Later at home I mulled over his daughter's visit. I was troubled by her hostility. Was her reproachful manner purely a demonstration of the utter despair she felt, or was there something else? Did she blame me for her father's condition?

'You're very pensive today?'

I was startled by Roopal's warm voice. I was quite literally lost in my thoughts. She was used to me cogitating the events of the day, and so when I replied 'Oh, it's nothing,' she smiled and went upstairs to settle Robert and Alex in their beds.

The night was restless. I thought back to the day, fifteen years earlier, when Eric Finch had humiliated his patient dying of lung cancer. Finch had played to the gallery of medical students gathered at the bedside and condemned the man's *smo*-king. I remembered the man's embarrassment as he was made to realise how he had only himself to blame for the tumour that grew within him. How would Finch have fared had he been in the clinician's chair, as I had that day, having an altercation with the patient's confrontational daughter? Perhaps there would not have such a polemic encounter: I could imagine the great surgeon fixing her with narrowed eyes and squashing her with a few but acerbic words.

My eyes were heavy but I couldn't sleep. What was it that Job, the Hebrew leader, had said? *When I lie down, I say, When shall I arise, and the night be gone? and I am full of tossings to and fro unto the dawning of the day.* Job had questioned the infliction of suffering on an innocent mankind while enduring great suffering himself. It occurred to me that perhaps Finch was doing likewise, the suffering inflicted by smoking more than he could bear.

I drifted off to sleep with the emphatic words and

syllables of a familiar verse peregrinating satisfyingly through my head.

> *Heredity, sex and age,*
> *Occupation, race and clime,*
> *The ills that men are subject to –*
> *The vices of our time.*

Goodnight, Mr Lodworski. Goodnight.

22

Yesterday the Hoover (well Dyson, then) packed up. The cause of this was at once obvious: its flex had been ripped from the electric plug, leaving the aforesaid plug still in the electric socket. Wasn't my fault – I blame the vacuum cleaner. The rubber cable had become increasingly taut as I journeyed with my Dyson to places afar within the house, until ping! – the wires wrenched themselves from the terminals in the plug.

I bought a super-duper plug from our local DIY store and set to work attaching it to the raw ends of wire poking from the flex. I over-tightened the earth, neutral and live terminals' screws and did likewise to those on either side of the little cable-retaining bridge so that their 'heads' were ground to nowt. Never mind, I thought, that's the point: the plug will never need to come off, will it? Unless this country should happen to adopt a different style of electrical socket for domestic use ...

I screwed up everything tightly and paused to admire the permanence of my work. Ho hum! Now all I had to do was put the lid on the plug.

Oh poo! The cable must first be threaded through a hole in the lid – a task made impossible, judging by the heap of brass filings that once were the tidy cross-shaped grooves on the twin screws' heads. There was only one thing for it: thread the cable through from the other end.

I dismantled the Dyson and extricated the flex from its moorings inside the inner workings of the machine. Easy! I then threaded the lid through and secured it to the plug's base. But then I couldn't remember how to re-assemble the bloody hoover – sorry – Hoover™ – OK *Dyson* then. No way could this be fixed under the manufacturer's warranty: my erstwhile meddling had invalidated that. Into the bin the whole lot went.

Enough self-deprecation! I say. It's someone else's turn. Let us suppose that some bloke – we'll call him Fred – happens to have a loose floor board that creaks whenever he walks on it. It's right by the bed and Fred can't avoid stepping on it. Fed up to the back teeth (the dental reference is deliberate, as you shall see) with the daily squeak, he decides to nail down the annoying board once and for all. He goes to his garage to get his 'ammer and some niyals, and then starts banging away to 'sortid ow-ert' (I'm not suggesting that Fred's a cockney, it just makes for a better story).

Oh bother of bothers: what should happen? Fred thinks he can hear a faint hissing sound. It definitely wasn't there before the fifth strike of his 'ammer but it sure is there now. He puts his ear to the floor and, make no mistake, dear friend, there's a definite hiss from under the boards. So Fred goes back into the garage, digs out a bolster and then attempts to lever out the board.

It's a funny thing, isn't it, how there are probably a hundred or so floor boards in Fred's semi-detached house, but the one board which *could* have been removed with ease is now the *most difficult* to remove? And this is because he's just made it so: for where there is usually one nail in place, he has driven five.

Cursing the fruits of 'is 'andiwork, Fred eventually pulls up the board, at once seeing the problem. He's punctured a gas pipe! 'Shit!' he says and quickly sticks a finger over the 'ole. 'Phew,' exhales Fred when the hissing stops.

Now what? He thumbs through the Yellow Pages and calls an emergency plumber.

'Fix yer pipe? Yeah, course. No sweat.'

'How much, old sport?' (I told you Fred wasn't *necessarily* Cockney.)

There follows a sharp in-draw of breath, then: 'Eighty quid call-out charge. Parts and labour extra.'

Fred bangs the receiver down and replaces his finger on the hole in the pipe.

'I know!' he cries out as he realises the solution. There

is, you see, a decorator due to attend any minute to paint Fred's hallway. He'll ask him. He keeps his finger on the hole until, sure enough, the door bell rings announcing the arrival of the decorator.

'Hello, old chap,' greets Fred. (I've said Fred *might* be posh, haven't I?) 'Listen, I've made a bit of a boo-boo,' he says. Fred crouches over the exposed floorspace and brings the painter up to date with his sorry tale.

'So be a good chap,' continues Fred, 'and repair the pipe for me.'

'Hang on!' exclaims the painter, waving his roller-sponge in the direction of Fred's weary finger which is covering the punctured pipe. There are occasional flashes of white chewing gum from within the decorator's oral cavity. 'I'm a painter, mate, not a gas fitter. I ain't got a clue how to fix *that*.'

'Oh please,' urges Fred. 'I'll make you a nice cup of tea.'

Fred, from his position on the floor, has an unrivalled view of the decorator flicking the gum off his palate before resuming chewing. He can't help thinking that the man resembles a camel, monotonously masticating whilst pondering the vicissitudes of desert life. 'It wouldn't be safe,' argues the camel, 'for me to meddle with gas pipes. I don't know how to sweat the joints and fix 'em all up. No, I won't do it. I'm sticking to painting.'

'You just listen to me,' says Fred, getting hot under the collar. 'I'm not going to stay down here all bloody day. Help me out, won't you, just this once?'

The decorator pauses, replacing his roller back in the paint tray. 'Look,' he says eventually, pulling the chewing gum from between his teeth. 'All I can do is to stick this 'ere gum on it and patch it up temporary, like. It'll only hold for a day or so, but at least it means you won't have to lie there all day long with your finger over the 'ole. Right?'

'Oh thank you,' says Fred. 'I'm much obliged, I really am.'

'But it's only short-term, like. You must get a pro out ASAP.'

'Yes, sure. I will. How much do I owe you?'

'Nothing,' the camel grins, his smile absurdly different as if the gum had acted as a prop. 'Just that nice cup of tea you promised.'

Three days later Fred hears a 'thlop' as the gum comes off the pipe and the gas once more escapes from the hole. *Hiss hiss hiss hiss*. He hadn't yet replaced the floor board as the gas man would need access to the pipe, but then he hasn't bothered to call anyone.

But here's the stupidity of what Fred does next. He telephones the decorator!

'Hello, old sport,' he breathes into the mouth piece. 'Remember me? The chap with the gum on his hole.'

'You *what*?' grunts the decorator, glancing at his bedside clock. 04:22 glows from the bright LED. 'Who are you?'

'I gave you a cup of tea when you stuck your gum...'

'Oh you,' he groans. 'D'ya know what time it is? What on earth do you want?'

'The gum's fallen off. Will you please come round and stick a fresh piece on.'

I relate this story whenever I am asked to prescribe antibiotics for a dental abscess. Over the years I have seen hundreds of patients whose belief it is that they have a gum infection or suchlike and, like Fred, they demand a quick-fix cure, in the form of antibiotics.

'Why haven't you gone to the dentist?' I ask time and again.

'Because he can't see me until next week,' comes the reply. Or more grating: 'Because he charges and you don't. So I come to you, Dr Barrie. Good, innit?'

Dentists are professionally obliged, much as doctors are, to see emergency patients the same day. So a patient's excuse that there isn't an appointment to be had at the dental surgery doesn't wash with me. No – the real reason is money. The British public have long had an obsession with getting something for nothing. We all recognise the advertising slogan which screams that some object or other is 'free'.

There's no such thing as a free lunch, but by God will the British try! They don't seem to care that I am grossly incompetent at the management of dental conditions. I might easily misdiagnose a dental abscess requiring urgent incision and drainage, for a straightforward dental infection. And having reached a diagnosis of 'dental infection', I struggle to choose the best antibiotic; I would do best to prescribe a cocktail of drugs in the hope that one of them will work.

My mother, the microbiologist, has told me the common pathogens in the oral cavity and the antibiotics which are effective against them. But it is rare for me to get this far with my patient because I bite the bullet, so to speak. If I give medication which cures the problem, the patient will be sure to come back for a repeat supply when the problem recurs, especially if my treatment is free! And recur it will if I treat it, believe me!

Nope. The best advice is to tell the patient to seek professional advice from a dentist. After all, would you want a dentist to fix your Dyson?

23

Ask yourself whether you are happy,
and you cease to be so.

John Stuart Mill
1806–73

A recent survey by the Department of Health showed 322 unfilled GP posts in England and Wales, double the number of such vacancies that existed twelve months earlier. There were seven applicants for each vacant post in 2001: now just four doctors apply for each position. There are far worse examples: Hamish Meldrum, a popular GP in West Yorkshire, described how his practice ten years ago 'had fifty to sixty applications for a vacant post. Five years ago it was twenty but eighteen months ago we didn't have a single application.'

Low GP morale is to blame for the present crisis in GP recruitment and retention, and the effect that this exerts on the number of school leavers choosing medicine as a career can only worsen an already desperate situation.

Today's doctors are now so weary with their lot that they would rather their offspring follow an alternative and uncertain career-path than follow them into the medical profession.

In 1986 when I applied to St Thomas's Hospital Medical School, I did so in competition with eleven or twelve other applicants; in 2003, with an estimated 7,135 medical school places available, there will be just two applicants vying for each place. The present government recognises the urgency of rectifying those issues which threaten the future of the National Health Service, and the provision of local health facilities by GPs in particular, but seems curiously uninterested in doing anything about it. Instead we have Clinical Governance, various 'incentive schemes', National Service Frameworks (NSFs), copious edicts from the National Institute of Clinical Excellence (NICE) and a plethora of other pseudo-babble government-sanctioned jargon. The more acronyms the better: I've given you NICE – how about PAMs (Professions Allied to Medicine), ACT (Audit Co-ordinator Training), ASTROPUs (I won't bore you with this one), CHI (Commission for Health Improvement), NCAA (National Clinical Assessment Authority), HIMP, PEC and so on?

Sir William Osler, the great physician and father of bedside medical teaching who died in 1919, once said:

'One finger in the throat and one in the rectum makes a good diagnostician.' I practise with one finger on the pulse and t'other on a calculator, for I am encouraged to make savings for the ostensible enhancement of my patients' care. Enhancement of patient care? Pah! I have, for instance, been invited as part of the Clinical Governance Incentive Scheme (CGIS) to create a register of patients suffering from chronic lung disease (emphysema and chronic bronchitis), and then record various items of data on these patients. For this I am to be paid two pence per patient! Were I to attend a 'seminar' – this being another hoop through which I must jump – I would be paid an additional £50, the sum being shared with my partners and subject to taxation. What a delight!

Or I could choose 1b): 'recording of diabetes dataset … and … produce a plan to indicate how the team will improve the care of patients with diabetes during 2003–04. The plan should be no longer than one-side [sic] of A4 paper, using bullet points.' Incentive? The princely sum of £1 per diabetic patient.

I became a doctor because (strange as it may seem) I get a kick out of sifting through clues in a patient's history, then eliciting what often are the subtlest of signs by means of clinical examination, followed by the *thrill* of trying to formulate a diagnosis. A *competent and intelligent* diagnosis.

And *one* diagnosis: an idle doctor would ascribe each symptom to a separate diagnosis.

The challenge, for me at least, is to link all the complaints to a single pathological process and then enjoy the delicious satisfaction of seeing my prescribed treatment (uniquely effective for the condition) resulting in cure. Ah! Bliss…

Eric Finch, his voice dropped to a steely whisper, and his rounded shoulders stiffened by the enormity of what he was about to say, once told me: 'If eight different women were attacked in London in one particular month, it would be a fool of a detective to seek eight different suspects. I wouldn't put it past you to do something equally stupid.'

And there usually is a link. Take, for example, the old lady in A&E with a fractured neck of femur and shortness of breath. All too often I've seen an orthopaedic surgeon fix the broken hip, prescribe something (an inhaler, perhaps, or maybe a diuretic) to ease her breathing difficulties, and then discharge the woman to the care of her GP. One diagnosis, Finch would chide: in the old woman's case she might have an arrhythmia (irregular heart beat) causing her to both fall down and become short of breath.

The media seem happy to run only stories that are

critical of doctors, but I would assert that most of us are an enthusiastic and (reasonably!) competent lot. I enjoy being a doctor but loathe the heavy workload, endless form-filling and unnecessary paperwork; in short, all factors that combine to steal time which would be better spent with patients.

As we live longer, and more illness is treated within primary care, the burden on family doctors will increase. The crisis in NHS general practice is real and fearsome. The Government's response is typically bureaucratic: a new contract for GPs and the promise of greater through-put in medical schools in order to churn out more doctors. But there's no guarantee that these doctors will want to go into boring old general practice – far more likely that they will be attracted by the omnipotent 'sexiness' of hospital medicine. And besides, hospital doctors are *proper* doctors!

With one in five GPs planning to leave the profession within five years, the need to persuade medical students to choose general practice has never been greater. Yet medical students tell me that very little is being done to persuade them that general practice can be just as attractive as hospital medicine. In September 2002, the Health Minister joined forces with GP leaders to promote a career in general practice at a certain London medical school. The event, however, clashed with students' examinations and their clinical commitments, with the result that fewer than ten medical students attended the event, and the entire body of first and second year students missed it altogether as it took place before their term had commenced! The handful of students present had already chosen general practice, hence their interest and their attendance at the event.

Perhaps medical schools themselves should do more to improve the standing of general practice within their environs. A recent poll by the Royal College of General Practitioners found that forty-eight per cent of GPs thought that more medical students would take up general practice if they had had experience of primary care, perhaps 'sitting in' with a local GP, earlier in their training.

Tomorrow's doctors are unlikely to rush towards a career in primary care, and for those that do the new contract will ensure they work shorter hours and that their relationship becomes yet more impersonal. As an editorial in *The Daily Telegraph* put it: 'There will be fewer doctors to treat more patients. Only by restoring the status of GPs within the medical profession will the crisis facing general practice be resolved.'

So what of the new contract? Doctors' leaders and Government ministers have been negotiating this for months if not years. A two-stage ballot eventually took place: round one, held in 2002, saw fewer than half of the country's GPs accepting the proposed contract; the second vote, a year on, secured approval by doctors who favoured the proposals detailed in the contract. There is also the promise of better remuneration. The framework of the contract is being fine-tuned and costed in readiness for its imminent implementation.

The contract commits GPs to act as agents of the Government, rather than for our patients. Ironically, a recent Government survey demonstrated ninety-one per cent patient satisfaction with their GP – with ministers therefore diverting funds to secondary care (i.e. hospitals), where NHS failings are perhaps more obvious and certainly more tangible. 'OLD MAN LAY ON TROLLEY IN A&E FOR 28 HOURS' screams the unfailingly attention-grabbing headline.

GPs run the risk of neglect because of our relative success. A group of GPs, in their open letter to the broadsheets, wrote: 'This neglect and the associated control freakery of the Government and its local agencies threaten the very future of the GP service.' I am not sure I would go so far: indeed, I do maintain my faith in the Government to resolve the omnifarious problems faced by the family doctor of today. Low GP morale and high workload are genuine concerns and ensuring that they are addressed is rightly a prerequisite to the success of the new contract. The NHS Confederation and Downing Street in particular want desperately for the contract to succeed; so, too, do the doctors whose medical practice will have been forever changed.

Dr John Chishom, Chairman of the General Practitioners' Committee and 'chief negotiator' for the new contract, wrote to all GPs after the first ballot. In his letter he pleaded for healthy optimism:

> I am aware of the profession's increasing cynicism and disillusionment and that you need to see some light at the end of the tunnel. We met recently with the English Minister of Health, and we left him in no doubt that GPs need to be convinced that the Government is serious about addressing their concerns through the contract. The Minister has acknowledged this.

Acknowledgement is all very well, but *suit the action to the word, the word to the action.*

Letter to *The Times*, Monday August 12th, 2002

Sir

Last month I waited more than two hours at a hospital clinic to see the ophthalmologist for my annual check-up. Thirty or 40 other patients had also resigned themselves to equally long waits. Nobody complained: how could we? We were supplicants waiting for our 'free' NHS treatment.

The concept of choice in a 'free' NHS is fundamentally flawed. 'Community ownership' gives the patient no more choice than centralised state control. Choice comes with the power to spend money and demand service for it. The State spends my money and decides how long I must wait in line for treatment. The choices Mr Milburn writes about would give me no power to demand service.

Edward A Pickett
Woking, Surrey

Pickett of Woking is correct. Alan Milburn, then Health Secretary, recognised that the NHS has become a monopoly provider with little choice for patients. He wanted to put the patient in the driving seat, but surely the only way to achieve this is to let the patient (as a consumer) control the flow of money between himself and the care provider. The contract should be specifically between the patient and the health care organisation.

Furthermore, the investment required to meet the NHS's ever-increasing costs cannot continue to be met by taxation alone. The NHS is an expensive beast to keep alive, with newer techniques and medical breakthroughs costing vast sums of money. Another factor in the spiralling cost of the NHS is that the number of appointments made by patients has more than doubled in recent years: in 1988, patients made an average of 2.54 visits to their doctor. Today's figure is 5.94 a year.

The Government has doggedly refused to accept that the time has come (indeed, came some time ago) when the NHS can no longer be funded purely from the revenue gained from taxes. In Britain we must pay when we consult an optician, chiropractor, dentist or osteopath, so why should a visit to, and especially from, a doctor be free? Why should children, pregnant mothers and the elderly be exempt from paying a prescription charge? Children of fabulously wealthy parents obtain all their medicines free from the local pharmacist. Why? Wouldn't it be fairer if everyone, regardless of financial status, paid, say, twenty pence for a prescription, rather than fifteen per cent (or whatever proportion it is) of the population forking out £6.50?

A staggering 617 million items were dispensed on the NHS in England alone in 2002, costing the country nearly £6.8 billion. Incredible when you consider that the majority don't pay any prescription charges at all – and those who do only contribute about half of the drug's true cost.

I've a handful of patients who are poor in the true sense of the word. Not poor because they buy Tesco's own brand of ketchup, or take holidays in the United Kingdom as opposed to the sunny climes of the Mediterranean. Rather, poor in that their children are inadequately clothed and on occasion they have insufficient funds to feed their family. I practise in an affluent suburb of Greater London and admittedly there is but a small pocket of deprivation. But I have friends who are GPs in inner cities and qualify for additional funds – so-called 'deprivation payments' – such is the prevalence of poverty within their patient lists.

24

When I was working as a psychiatrist at West Park Hospital, I looked after a young man with paranoid schizophrenia who was already an inpatient when I took up my post. 'Max' (not his real name) was psychotic much of the time, and on ward rounds it troubled me to see his young mind tormented by auditory hallucinations which, later, I learned were incessant and insistent.

Sometimes he would shout in response to the voices within his head but most of the time he sat by his very ordinary bed (for psychiatric units do not have standard hospital-type beds), preoccupied with the continual banter that he alone could hear.

One morning, sometime in early October 1992, I spoke to Max's parents. I discussed his drug treatment and suggested that we might try a different agent, perhaps something from one of the other pharmacological classes within the psychotropic armamentarium. His parents were pleased by my interest in their son and grateful, too, to have been involved in his management. We discussed the drug's side effects and I made the necessary amendment to Max's drug chart.

The response was impressive: within a fortnight the young man demonstrated clarity of thought, orientation and awareness of his surroundings, and was able to interact conversationally with his family. I spent many hours on the ward with Max, examining his mental state by clinical assessment − a veritable 'toolbag' to probe a person's psyche − and there was no doubting his apparent recovery. No longer were the voices in his head consuming his everyday cognition: he was able now to tell me much more about his auditory hallucinations − or, simply, 'voices'.

On his previous drug cocktail he had been too deluded and certainly too thought-disordered to converse rationally, and I realised that the voices had been unremitting and painfully relentless. Schizophrenics experience three different types of auditory hallucination. Max was describing *running commentary* − the other two being *echo de pensées* (the person hears his own thoughts, as an echo, spoken aloud within his head) and *third person* (such as: 'So, you're going to make a telephone call, are you? Look, he's washing his hands now. No wait, he's not now because we said he was and he heard us. He's trying to trick us. Ah, now he *is* going to wash…')

Running commentary hallucinations, as the name suggests, take the form of a continuous soundtrack. The voices interfere with normal thought processing, itself disordered by the schizophrenic mind, and it was only when Max's 'voices' had lessened that the young man on my ward was able to give a clear account.

I was conscious, however, of the unfavourable environment that existed at West Park Hospital. The majority of the inpatients were long-term residents who portrayed, en masse, a pitiful image of social neglect and institutionalisation. My patient was improving day by day in response to the new medication and was cognisant of the scene around him. It was clear to me that his progress would be hampered by the oppressive atmosphere at West Park.

I tried in vain to find a bed for Max at Epsom Hospital, a district general hospital, but my ward there was mostly full of neurotic teenagers and anxious thirty-something-year-olds, and the last bed had gone just a few days earlier to Ted Leonard, the man with visual hallucinations. I had resisted admitting Mr Leonard to West Park for much the same reason. I spoke to my boss, Dr Mary Chisham, a lovely woman who has to be one of the nicest consultants for whom I have ever worked, and she agreed that the kindest option would be to discharge Max and follow his progress in the outpatient clinic.

Towards the end of September, therefore, I discharged my patient from West Park on the proviso that he return one week later to my clinic. His parents shook my hand warmly and expressed their gratitude for my giving them back a son whom they feared had been lost to an eternal and forlorn vegetative state.

When, a few days later, he failed to show up for the second time in my clinic, I feared the worst. After he had missed the first appointment I made sure the clerk sent him the details of a further one; I was worried that Max might have relapsed, all too common in schizophrenia, due to non-compliance with medication. With some conditions the symptoms are so unbearable that sufferers resume taking their medication immediately following an unintentional break, but those with mental illness feel so well whilst taking pills that they eventually forget the importance of continuing with them. Once a patient suffers a relapse, then insight into their condition is lost and with it all hope of subsequent treatment compliance.

I telephoned Max's GP to inquire whether he had seen Max since his discharge from West Park Hospital. No, he said, he hadn't been to the surgery for some months. I had only given Max a small supply of medication as I knew he was returning to my clinic and now I fretted that he would run out of the drug which was keeping his mind on an even keel. I decided that the only option would be to visit him at home.

I telephoned before setting off and his parents confided that Max's mind had already begun to deteriorate. He had finished the supply of medication I had given him, and although Max denied it, they suspected that he was once again hearing voices.

My car was being serviced but fortunately a colleague offered to drive me the short distance to his house. The colleague, a young lady doctor who had duties similar to my own, had parked quite legitimately in front of the large Victorian hospital building. To our astonishment there was a metal parking clamp applied to her front nearside wheel.

I went at once to the Unit Manager and demanded an explanation.

'Sorry,' he quipped, shaking his head from side to side. 'Can't discuss that. Policy, you know.'

'I'm sorry?' I asked.

'Like I say,' said the Unit Manager. 'Can't discuss it.'

'But Dr Khraishi and I have a sick patient to visit.'

The administrator looked at me blankly, relishing the fact that as I hadn't posed a question, there was no obligation on him to give a response.

'So what shall I do?' I implored.

'Pay the release fee,' he said.

I was dammed if I was going to pay a release fee! Dr

Khraishi demurred. 'Perhaps we should,' she said quietly to me. 'It might be the easiest way out of this mess.'

'Like hell we're going to pay that twit,' I said, walking around the car and wondering if there might be another way.

I air-called Mary Chisham and waited by the wall-mounted telephone alongside switchboard for her return call.

'Whatever you do, Michael, I'll support you,' came her response at last. 'Your priority is to your patients, and not to a jumped-up manager.'

Walking back to the car, it occurred to me that a wheel clamp is applied usually to the body of the tyre; it follows, therefore, that if the tyre can be made smaller then the clamp would surely be too loose. A third doctor, Paul Rankin, had emerged from the postgraduate library to see what the commotion was about. Paul – now a GP in Woking, and an eminently sensible chap with a decent awareness of right and wrong – agreed that if the tyre was deflated, the clamp could be removed.

Dr Khraishi wasn't convinced that we were doing the right thing but Heck, I said to her, we need to get the damned thing off your car; and I didn't see why she, or indeed any of us, should have to pay to achieve this.

I jacked the back end of the car up so that the clamped

wheel was raised just off the ground and then pressed the valve to release most of the air. Paul helped me to ease the metal clamp;. its once firm grip now loosened and it slid off easily. It was October and our hands were cold and numb. The clamp was mudsplattered and wet but I picked it up and carried it towards the main hospital block.

'Where are you going with that?' cried Paul. 'Just leave it by the side of the parking space.'

'No fear!' I called back to him. 'This'll be too good to miss!' The clamp was heavy but I manhandled it through the main entrance and then onwards to the administrator's office.

I would have knocked but I didn't have a free hand as both were firmly applied to the clamp's sides. I pushed the Unit Manager's door open with my foot − an act which must have appeared ruder than I'd intentioned − and approached his desk. My hands were frozen now and my fingers were beginning to lose their grip on the large, unwieldy metal object. I was afraid that I might drop it onto my toes − which would certainly preclude a visit to Max − and in a sudden moment of apparent indecision, whilst the manager looked at me with an expression of startled and indignant expectation, I lifted the clamp up and onto his leather-embossed desk and dropped it amongst his neatly-stacked papers.

I had just enough time to see the bespattering of mud

caused by the forceful impact of the clamp's descent, and the dripping of soiled rain water over the edge of the desk, before turning away and heading back to Dr Khraishi's car.

The hospital management committee was furious with the junior doctors – me especially – and there followed much debate, two extraordinary meetings and the inevitable pleonastic correspondence.

It would be nice if I could tell you that this was the end of my parking difficulties at West Park and Epsom Hospitals, but this would be but a half-truth. For whilst there were no further problems at the former, the same cannot be said of the Epsom site, where they could at times be insurmountable.

I *can* say, however, that Max agreed to restart his medication and to attend my clinic. His improvement was maintained, and as in the ending of most meritorious fables: everyone lived happily ever after.

★　★　★

Department of Paediatrics
Epsom Hospital

Mr Martin White
General Services Manager
Epsom Hospital   15th July 1993

Dear Mr White

Further to our telephone conversation last week, I should like to ask whether your staff could refrain from placing their 'polite notices' under my windscreen wiper.

As I am sure you are aware, I try diligently each morning to park my car in a 'designated' zone. Since the new scheme was introduced, however, I have yet to find a place in any of the appropriate car parks. It is interesting to note that prior to the new scheme I was always able to park my car *somewhere*. As we discussed on the telephone there are bound to be inevitable teething problems, but I am finding the daily photocopied notice which states 'please ensure that you park correctly in future' a little irksome.

Yours sincerely

(signed)

Dr M Barrie

Department of Paediatrics
Epsom Hospital

Mr Martin White
General Services Manager
Epsom Hospital   26th July 1993

Dear Mr White

... I was a little perturbed by today's notice on my car which read 'Wheel Clamping is imminent for those vehicles not conforming to the new parking arrangements'. Instructions which emanated from your own office quite recently made it clear that those cars who use the Visitors Car Park as an 'overflow' are expected to pay. Today's statement that staff who park within an incorrect zone will be clamped, presumably with a costly release fee, is naturally quite disturbing...

Above all, my sole commitment to the Hospital is a statutory obligation to treat and care for patients. It would be sad if I were to be unable to meet this responsibility through an inability to park my car without paying excessive charges...

However, I do feel it only appropriate to conclude that I would inform members of the local Press and local newspapers should my vehicle be clamped whilst on the call of duty.

With best wishes

Yours sincerely

(signed)

Dr Michael Barrie

Estates Department
Epsom Hospital

27th July 1993

Dr M Barrie
Department of Paediatrics
Epsom General Hospital

Dear Dr Barrie

Thank you for your letter of the 15th July.

It is very difficult for me to instruct my staff to select one particular vehicle and ensure that a polite notice is not placed on the windscreen.

The demand for staff spaces far outnumbers the spaces available and the possession of a permit does not guarantee a parking space.

... Additional spaces have now been provided in the Maternity car park and shortly a number of extra spaces will be made available in the main car park...

Yours sincerely

(signed)

Martin White
General Services Manager

On September 20 1993 I parked my car on a grassy area to the edge of one of the hospital's car parks. Sometime during the course of the day my car was clamped.

Department of Paediatrics
Epsom Hospital

Mr Martin White
General Services Manager
Epsom Hospital   3rd November 1993

Dear Mr White

I wonder if it might be possible to stop individuals from parking their cars in a linear fashion along the two middle 'lanes' of the main front (yellow) car park. These are unmarked for parking, and make it difficult for even a small car to manoeuvre into a designated place. Furthermore, a number of cars are blocking the exit to the front of the hospital by parking on the double yellow lines. These cars, and the ones in non-designated areas above, cause far more obstruction and inconvenience than cars parked innocuously on grassed areas.

Yours sincerely

(signed)

Dr Michael Barrie

Estates Department
Epsom Hospital

1st December 1993

Dr M Barrie
Epsom Hospital

Dear Dr Barrie

Further to your letter of the 3rd November,
wheelclamping will commence very shortly for *all*
illegally parked cars, including those parked in the
fashions which you mention.

Yours sincerely

(signed)

Martin White
General Services Manager

Department of Paediatrics
Epsom Hospital

1st January 1994

Dr Tudor Thomas
Chief Executive
Epsom Hospital

Dear Dr Thomas

I am in receipt of your two communications to all members of staff (15th and 16th December 1993) concerning the matter of car parking on the Hospital site. As you are probably aware, Mr Martin White and myself have corresponded on this subject, and you should have received copies of some of these letters. I wonder if, without wishing to labour the point, I may make some further comments...

... To my amazement, I was clamped whilst parked on a *grassed* area. Fortunately the British Medical Association agreed that a car cannot be clamped for so-called 'illegal' parking unless *each* such area is marked as such. There are still no 'keep off grass' signs by the area in question. On every single day since I was clamped, cars continue to park on the identical patch of grass without being clamped. Perhaps I was a convenient scapegoat...

With all good wishes for the New Year.

Yours sincerely

(signed)

Dr Michael Barrie

Epsom Hospital

7th January 1994

Dr M Barrie
Epsom Hospital

Dear Dr Barrie

Thank you for taking the time and trouble to write to me concerning your views on our car parking.

... We are attempting to control the access to our hospital in the most acceptable and expeditious fashion for emergency vehicles, patients, their visitors and our own staff.

If, however, cars are parked illegally, i.e. in areas (such as grassed areas/yellow lined roadways) which are not marked up as parking areas, then we will be using our powers to clamp.

It is clear that with goodwill and perseverance on everyone's part, we can cope.

Yours sincerely

(signed)

Dr Tudor E. Thomas
Chief Executive

25

Dr Soundara Pandian was a general practitioner in Chessington, a neighbouring town to Kingston upon Thames, and his practice bordered mine. He was popular with his patients, who appreciated his sense of fun, impressive clinical expertise and unselfish approach to the care he gave them. His was a familiar face at local GP meetings; he was respected by colleagues both in general practice and at the hospital where he worked as a qualified, and accomplished, surgeon.

Soundara qualified in Madras in 1983 and obtained fellowships of the Royal Colleges of Surgeons of London, Edinburgh and Glasgow. Such an 'FRCS hat-trick' is no mean feat: each examination has a pass rate of around twenty per cent and his ability to pass all three never once affected his unfailing modest and reserved manner. He was the epitome of a perfect doctor and a loving father to his two children – a five-year-old girl and her younger brother, aged one.

In April 2002, whilst walking along Chessington's main thoroughfare, Soundara Pandian experienced a most terrible headache of such sudden onset that it caused him to fall to the ground. He had had a subarachnoid haemorrhage. He was just forty-two years old.

The following is an abridged version of an account which later appeared in the local newspaper, *The Kingston Guardian*:

Chessington and Hook was rocked by the untimely loss of much-loved GP, Doctor Soundara Pandian, on Sunday April 7. He was very popular, easy-going and friendly. We will miss Pandy's energy, enthusiasm and friendship. He was held in high regard in Kingston, and especially in Chessington where he was a friend and part of the local community as much as a family doctor.

A few years earlier, one of the consultants for whom I had worked at Epsom died, also of a subarachnoid haemorrhage. He was in the outpatient department when he developed an intense pain in the back of his head. Realising that he might be having a cerebral bleed, he began walking the short route to the hospital's A&E department. He never made it and his young family, much as Soundara Pandian's had, mourned the premature end to his life, whilst the hospital lamented the untimely loss of a talented gynaecologist.

Maggie Halsall, my patient, taught me much about the ethical dilemmas of looking after someone with a berry aneurysm. I'd thought she was lucky: after all, when she was just twenty-one she had survived a potentially-fatal subarachnoid haemorrhage. But as she herself ruefully conceded, her risks weren't over. In the event she decided against an operation to clip her aneurysm – but it's a Catch 22 situation. The reality of an undiagnosed berry aneurysm is the catastrophe of a family losing a loved one without warning. Like my great-grandfather, who was killed when he was knocked down by a brewery's horse and cart, there are men who will kiss their wife and children goodbye at the start of a day that, unbeknownst to them, will be their last.

Harry Trendle was a retired police officer. He was often at the surgery as his wife had inexorable hip problems that had begun with pain from osteoarthritis and culminated in a botched joint-replacement operation. I tinkered around with her painkillers and her husband would be dispatched to pick up the prescription. The new pills would work for a couple of weeks and then Mrs Trendle would ask that they be changed, and so the cycle continued.

'Mr Trendle's at reception. Can you come please?' said

the new girl on the front desk. Mr Trendle usually spent a few minutes chatting and joking with the receptionists before having his ailing wife's prescription dispensed at the pharmacy. I had often wondered whether Mrs Trendle's chronic pain was causing him emotional ruin; on more than one occasion I had asked him if he was depressed. He always laughed at the suggestion, though I sometimes wondered whether his ebullient denial was a silent cry for help.

I said, 'What's the matter?' adding, 'His wife's prescription is in the usual place.'

'No,' said my receptionist. 'He's not feeling well and he's being sick and he's … Oh shit! Come quickly!'

I muttered an apology to the patient I was with at the time, and raced to the reception desk outside. One advantage of working in an old Victorian building is the absence of an open–plan layout and the lack of privacy this affords. Mr Trendle had collapsed amidst a pool of vomit, and my partner, who had also been summoned by the frightened girl at reception, helped me carry him into a consulting room and lay him gently on the couch.

I felt pleased that Mr Trendle's modesty had been maintained throughout by the simple act of closing the waiting room door: quite a contrast to the spectacle that would have occurred in a modern health centre where there is a common reception-cum-seating atrium with doctors' rooms arranged peripherally.

Mr Trendle was in a coma. I checked his vital signs: blood pressure, pulse and temperature – three parameters that tell a doctor so much about his patient's condition. Mr Trendle's blood pressure was on the high side and his pulse was steady at fifty beats per minute. His elevated blood pressure and bradycardia rang an alarm bell in my mind, and I moved quickly on to his neurological system. His unconscious state precluded me from performing any of the tests so beloved of neurologists. The 'touch your nose with your index finger and then do the same with your eyes closed and … er, that's it … and now touch *my* index finger …' kind of thing.

Mr Trendle had one other very significant clinical sign: he demonstrated papilloedema – swelling, as seen with an ophthalmoscope, of the optic disc in the retina of the eye. Papilloedema, together with his slow pulse and hypertension, suggested that Mr Trendle had raised pressure within his skull. Determination of its cause, for instance a brain tumour, abscess or haemorrhage, was unimportant. The priority was to arrange his urgent transfer to A&E.

An ambulance whisked Mr Trendle to hospital, where a brain scan showed a large bleed into the space under the arachnoid membrane. He was transferred, as Maggie

Halsall had been some thirty years earlier, to the neuro-surgical team; but, unlike her, was not left to languish untreated in a hospital bed. No, Mr Trendle was managed by highly skilled doctors in a high-tech London neurosciences unit – not that it was to do him much good.

It is conventional wisdom not to operate on an unconscious patient. Surgery in this situation is hazardous. The consultant neurosurgeon looking after Mr Trendle therefore spent the next few days preparing him for theatre: an angiogram was performed to determine the site of the subarachnoid haemorrhage and whether there were other concomitant berry aneurysms; his blood pressure was controlled with intravenous drugs; and his hydration ensured with isotonic fluids.

Mr Trendle recovered consciousness on the sixth day (considerably quicker than Mrs Halsall) and the consultant told him about the events following his visit to my surgery.

'Incredible, absolutely incredible,' was all he kept saying. 'I can remember going to collect my wife's prescription at the surgery but nothing after that.'

'You vomited and then lost consciousness. Dr Barrie says you went out like a light.' The neurosurgeon smiled.

'Incredible,' said Mr Trendle again, and the surgeon explained the planned operation.

'Blimey!' said Mr Trendle. 'But I feel so well now. Do I really need it?'

Mr Trendle had, it has to be said, made an apparently complete recovery but the consultant was reserved in his optimism. 'You've been very fortunate to get this far. About thirty per cent of people like you, that's a third, die on the spot. Another third die within a week which,' he added ruefully, 'for you is today or tomorrow.'

'Oh,' said Mr Trendle disconsolately. 'But if I make it past the next couple of days I'm safe, right?'

'Not necessarily. One in three patients with a subarachnoid haemorrhage has another brain haemorrhage, and only one in three of these survives.'

'You make it sound more risky than my old job in the police force.'

Mr Trendle was taken to theatre the next day. Most specialists are anxious not to drag things out into the second week as this is the time of a potential re-bleed. His scalp was shaved and an incision made in the skull over the site of the aneurysm, now sealed temporarily by clotted blood, and a clip was applied to the neck of the aneurysm. The wound was closed and the patient wheeled out to the recovery area. It was a three-hour operation but all seemed to have gone well.

Mr Trendle was slow to wake up from his anaesthetic

but his vital signs were stable and there was no evidence of another bleed. Both the initial scan in A&E and the angiogram had only shown the one aneurysm so, unless the clip had fallen off, a further haemorrhage was unlikely.

At 4 o'clock his wife arrived, brought in a wheelchair by their daughter-in-law, and he opened his eyes in recognition of her voice. The nurses were alarmed that their patient could lift his eyelids in response to commands and yet he could not move his limbs.

'Can you smile, Mr Trendle?' asked the charge nurse.

He could not.

'Can you say something? Anything,' came the next question. The nurse's tone was that of gentle encouragement.

He could not.

The charge nurse bleeped the senior house officer, who examined Mr Trendle and then arranged an urgent brain scan. Fifteen per cent of patients who have an operation to clip an aneurysm either have a stroke from the operation or die. The MRI scan pictures were unequivocal: Harry Trendle had had a stroke.

His wife telephoned me at the surgery that afternoon. I thought about telling her about my colleague in Chessington who had just died, but then thought better of it. She has enough to worry her, and my well-meant effort to reassure her might have the opposite effect. Your husband has survived, is what I said, and told her that I would meet her at the hospital the next day.

We spent some time at her husband's bedside and I could see from his clinical state that recovery, at least in the neurological sense, was unlikely. He had a dense hemiplegia – paralysis of one side of his body – and was unable to communicate other than by blinking his eyes.

Later, back in the surgery, I made a telephone call to St Thomas's Hospital. The medical school's existence might have crumbled but the hospital remains a centre of clinical excellence, with a first-class department of neurology and neuro-rehabilitation. St Thomas's is the official hospital for the Metropolitan Police and I reckoned that Mr Trendle, a retired police officer, might be granted more individualistic care. It was evident that he would need an intensive programme of occupational therapy, speech therapy and physiotherapy, as well as psychological help and dietetic support. The team coordinator to whom I spoke was most helpful and offered to assess my patient.

'Thank you, Dr Barrie,' his daughter-in-law said a few days later. 'But Mum and I would rather stick with the hospital he's at already. The nurses know him well, as do the doctors too, and it's much nearer for us to visit.'

'Yes,' I agreed, realising that central London wouldn't

be an easy journey for Mrs Trendle by car or by train. Her hip pain had worsened since her husband's collapse at the surgery.

Mr Trendle is home now; and has a full complement of supporting services from my district nurse and the community physiotherapist. He cannot talk or walk or feed himself, and it is his daughter-in-law now who visits the practice on behalf of her mother and father.

I suspect Mr Trendle wishes he had taken his chances without an operation.

I suspect, too, that he is depressed – who wouldn't be in his state? – but when I ask him to blink twice for 'yes' or once for 'no', he just grunts and I suspect it is his attempt to laugh off my suggestion, just as he used to before.

I suspect he may have seen Maggie Halsall as she checked in at reception but, like all patients, whether in hospital or a GP's surgery, hers would have been one more anonymous face amongst the others who come, day in and day out, to see me at my surgery. He couldn't possibly have guessed her diagnosis, what they had in common, or the operation she never had – either thirty years ago or now.

I suspect all manner of things.

26

Sometime in the summer of 1987, a Scot from Falkirk was found collapsed in a London street. Alexander Fallon, a heavy drinker who had lived in and out of hostels following the death of his wife thirteen years earlier, was rushed to Royal London Hospital in Whitechapel, east London. He'd had a subarachnoid haemorrhage.

Fallon underwent emergency surgery and, much like Harry Trendle, had a metal clip inserted to stem the bleeding inside his brain. He recovered well from his operation and, after a period of convalescence spent with his daughter, Fallon was back in London. He would stick around London's King's Cross Station, welcoming fellow Scots as they arrived by train in the hope that they might give him enough change for a packet of cigarettes or a drink.

He kept in touch with his daughters, two of whom live in America; in his letters he would ask that they send him money at various hostels across the capital. Fallon was also in receipt of state benefit.

In November 1987, the same year that Fallon suffered his brain haemorrhage, Britain witnessed one of the worst fires yet on the London Underground. The King's Cross fire began amongst dry rubbish in a machine room below a wooden escalator and it rapidly spread to engulf the entire ticket hall concourse. In the panic that ensued, passengers tried to escape by means of escalators but these delivered them fatally into the blazing fire; others, running to avoid the flames, became trapped in the many dead ends of the Tube's labyrinthine tunnels.

Thirty-one people died in the tragedy. Police have been able to identify all but one of the fire's victims: the body of the thirty-first victim eludes them. The charred remains of Body 115, so-called after his mortuary tag at University College Hospital, were found the morning after the fire and for sixteen years his identity (the autopsy at least knows that it was a man) has baffled police authorities. Detectives have followed more than two thousand leads from Ireland to the Far East in their quest to discover the name of Body 115 and have even circulated details of his dentures to all of Britain's twenty-five thousand dentists.

The mystery as to Body 115's identity may soon, however, be unravelled. Forensic experts say that Body 115 was a smoker, aged about sixty at death and probably about 5 feet 2 inches in height. Fallon was seventy-two at the time of the fire, a cigarette smoker, and his relatives reckon he was 5 feet 3 inches tall. His photograph bears an uncanny resemblance to the reconstructed images of Body 115's face.

Fallon's letters and phone calls home ceased in 1987, with no contact since the night of the fire. Furthermore, no benefits have been claimed in his name since the tragedy. And, crucially, the pathologist performing the post-mortem on Body 115 found a metal clip in his head, meaning he'd had surgery to arrest a subarachnoid haemorrhage.

Could it be that Alexander Fallon is the last unidentified victim of the King's Cross fire?

Just a few days ago I saw a little girl with chickenpox. Her mother hadn't come for a diagnosis, for the rash was clearly that of chickenpox, but rather for my advice on whether she could attend nursery.

'Of course,' I had said. 'But you'll undoubtedly have a struggle with the nursery staff.'

'I already have,' sighed the mother nonchalantly. 'Can't see why, though. I mean she *got* the blasted infection there, so why keep her away?'

I nodded in agreement. I used to regularly telephone the local nurseries and tell them the harm they were causing by their insistence that kids with chickenpox stay away. I would describe the scenario: a child has chickenpox. The nursery say 'we don't want your child here whilst he or she is infectious', so the child's playmates do not get exposed to the virus and enter adulthood non-immune to chickenpox.

The consequences can indeed be dire. Firstly, chickenpox caught during adulthood has a higher rate of serious complications and a higher death rate. Secondly, and perhaps more tragically, the outcome of a pregnancy in a non-immune woman exposed to the infection whilst carrying her unborn child is disastrous.

I would say all this to the nursery staff but they were never interested. All I would get was a whole load of mumbo-jumbo about teachers 'catching shingles from chickenpox' (impossible!) or children with leukaemia catching the infection and their weakened immune systems not being able to cope (pretty unlikely).

'Ah,' the head teacher of one primary school had said. 'What about staff who might just be pregnant?'

'Most women have already had chickenpox, in which case there isn't a risk,' I replied. *Unless they went to a school such as yours, which means they might well not be immune*, I thought of adding.

'Say they haven't had chickenpox?' asked the woman, reading my mind.

'They've probably had it and forgotten, but to be sure I

would suggest that you instruct all teaching staff who think they haven't had chickenpox to stay indoors from the moment they discontinue their contraception until the day of delivery. They mustn't go outside lest they meet any children with chickenpox. No trips to the shops or to the cinema or to the theatre…'

I heard a click. 'Hello?' I'd said into the phone.

She had hung up.

What of the future, then? The question beloved of interviewers is, 'Where do you see yourself in fifteen years?' I am in my thirties; God willing, I have years ahead of me in general medical practice. 'God willing', for who knows what lurks around the next corner? The untimely deaths of Soundara Pandian and the gynaecologist at Epsom are reminders of how a young life can be extinguished with such unjust abruptness.

At Ruth's funeral – my young patient with breast cancer – the priest read those thought-provoking lines from St Mark's gospel: 'Watch ye therefore: for ye know not when the master of the house cometh, at even, or at midnight, or at the cockcrowing, or in the morning: lest coming suddenly he find you sleeping. And what I say unto you I say unto all: Watch.' Haunting words.

So good health assumed, will I stick it out as a GP? There's still a lot of work to be done to improve the lot of the family doctor. It isn't, by any stretch of the imagination, a 'cushy' job. The endless stream of sick patients can be tiring and irksome; yes, it is 'what the job's all about', but the constant pressure put upon GPs is relentless and leads to ultimate burnout.

A typical GP with two thousand patients on his list might see fifty patients in a day, with a home visit or two somehow crammed into his day. It might well take an hour to perform just a single visit, as invariably one gets stuck in traffic when the roads are at their busiest. Seventy per cent of consultations are for self-limiting illnesses, which would suggest, you might think, that educating the patient on the self-management of common ailments would lower the return-visit rate. My experience is that is not the case.

I offer my patients a ten-minute slot but all too often this is eroded by customary niceties: Hello, Mrs Brown, how are you? Oh, fine thanks. And you? You're running late today, doctor. I mustn't keep you, but how *are* the children? Your younger one, what's he called again? What? Ah yes, Alex, he must be nearly four now...' And so on. Now there's just a few minutes in which to deal with Mrs Brown's problem. 'Problem, doctor? No no, you don't understand; I've a list! Let me see … Oh yes, first I want to ask about my blood pressure pills. They…'

Some patients will happily trot out five separate problems, each of which properly deserves a full ten minutes, but because of the earlier chit-chat there are now only six minutes remaining! It will take two minutes to write up the consultation record, so that leaves just four minutes. *Four minutes for five problems.*

What to do? There are two options – or so most people seem to think. Spend less than one minute dealing with each item on Mrs Brown's list – and hence misdiagnose and in turn mistreat her due to sloppiness. Or give each problem the ten minutes it merits. Five times ten equals fifty: fifty minutes! Do this just a few times each day and the result is that the doctor runs five hours late! Imagine the outcry: 'It's not good enough, Mabel. My doctor's appointment was for ten this morning but he didn't see me until four o'clock in the afternoon!'

There is another, better, option. 'We'll try and do one of the things on your list,' I say, 'and if there's time *maybe* one other. For the rest, Mrs Brown, you'll have to rebook.' Most patients are fine with my approach, although there is the occasional one who is horrified that I won't address their assorted ills, which they've saved up especially for their annual pilgrimage to my surgery, and there then ensues a half-hour debate on how appalling the NHS is – and another half-hour moaning that I'm an arrogant, big-headed oaf.

Do this a few times in one day...

Things have to change, then, if the problem of recruitment and retention of family doctors is going to improve. I love my work and I love treating patients; I hate, on the other hand, government interference in the way I care for them. I detest red-tape and form-filling and unnecessary paperwork, and I detest the never-ending jumping through hoops to show that I am complying with Whitehall's targets and less-than-gleaming reforms. All that glitters is not gold...

With increasing consumerism, both within the NHS and without, there's a real need to educate the public as to what a GP can realistically be expected to achieve and what lies squarely outside his remit. Mindful of these caveats, I wish to give it my best shot.

Let's return momentarily to the British public. Doors in public places tend, nowadays, to either be made of glass or at least have a glass window set within them. I step aside should I see that someone is approaching from the other side. My gesture is intended to be more courteous than chivalrous, notwithstanding a profligate desire, of course to avoid a bumping of bodily forms. Here is my gripe:

why is it that I am forced to play subservient doorman to the throng of people who then push through the door that I hold open?

Do I hear an utterance of gratitude? Or observe a smile or nod of thanks? Do I ever! Much the same with the action – or inaction – of fellow motorists. Where is this leading, you might be wondering? To the behaviour of a minority of patients: those who consider it their God-given right to first-class medical care, naturally at no cost to themselves, where the dutiful little doctor must go out of his way to satisfy them. I said much earlier in this book that the lay definition of a 'good doctor' is far removed from the words a colleague might employ.

It is the present government's wish that patients should be able to see a GP within forty-eight hours. No one knows where this number came from; where has it been shown, for instance, that the quality of care improves should a patient be seen at forty-two hours compared with, say, fifty hours. But wait! A government-funded study by a team from Manchester University showed that patient expectation is exceeding the government's forty-eight hour target. Seven out of ten patients were not satisfied at having to wait forty-eight hours to see their doctor and, incredibly, almost one-third were not happy to wait until the next day.

It gets worse: one-third were upset that they were kept waiting in the waiting room for five minutes; and seventy-one per cent reckoned that a ten-minute delay was unacceptable! Patients' expectations might be increasing, but no more than is mirrored across society.

And such expectations have invaded my clinical practice. There can't be a waitress in the world who hasn't brought the wrong dish to a table, or a postman who delivers the wrong letter to the wrong house, and so on. I know that on many an occasion I have ordered something from a shop only for some unrelated item to arrive from the warehouse. I don't cause a scene as anybody can make a mistake and, in any case, to do so would result in a shrug of the shoulders accompanied by murmurs of 'these things can happen'. But wait! These same waitresses, postmen and shopkeepers are patients too. Try giving one of them the wrong drug and in so doing cause terrible harm; and then try shrugging it off with 'it's just one of those things'. Aha! Wouldn't work, would it?

I have thought often about this paradox and reckon upon only two possibilities. Either other people look upon their own jobs as inferior to mine and so take the view that it doesn't matter if they make a mistake – but hell it sure does if the doctor does. Or (just as unlikely) their job *does* matter yet they are careless – but expect their doctor not to be. No: the answer is much more simple. It may be a cliché but we're all human and 'mistakes do happen'. It's just bad luck if you're an airline pilot or brain surgeon as the shit will *always* hit the fan when things go wrong.

Morning surgery has begun. The first patient is Vince, Mrs Halsall's son-in-law, whose tennis elbow I injected last week with a mixture of steroids and local anaesthetic. Today is a planned review: a patient coming to see me at *my* request, not theirs. The response is better than I'd expected and he has made a successful return to work. Vince is a despatch driver for a local engineering works. He used to work at St Thomas's Hospital but that's another story ...

The name of my next patient is unfamiliar. Perhaps he's a newcomer to the practice. Newly registered, new problems, new challenges. I sigh and call him in.

EPILOGUE

Not so very long ago, I was asked by an A-level student whether she might 'sit in' with me whilst I saw patients. Requests to use my surgery as a venue for such 'work experience' were once numerous, typically coming from careers advisors at schools, but most resulted in dismal assignments and I had begun to sense that many patients objected to the presence of an unfamiliar face in the consulting room. Thus work experience, compulsory for all pupils over the past ten years yet damned as 'boring' by the CBI in 2003, had died a death as far as my involvement was concerned.

Then Amy came along. Her father was at that time driving the 'out of hours' doctor's vehicle, an ordinary car kitted out with numerous gizmos which was used to ferry the emergency doctor to those too sick (or, more commonly, too lazy) to attend the local primary healthcare centre. He and I had spent many a long winter's evening in that car, criss-crossing the roads of south-west London, and I was only too pleased to acquiesce to his daughter's request.

Amy had the prescience to say that she might not want to be a doctor; a few days spent in general practice would help her, she said, to make up her mind. She was bright, and eager to enrich her mind with the practice of a subject which she might not pursue.

We had discussed the aetiology of depression and I related Finch's rhyme, adding that I had had the fortune to have been taught by one of London's greatest surgeons. Amy was captivated by my praiseful account of Finch and inquired where I thought he had first heard it. I shrugged, and we most probably talked about the chemical treatment of depression.

It wasn't until July 2002, when this book at last had evolved from a pre-conceptual stage to an embryological one, that I set about answering Amy's question: to discover the origin of *that* rhyme. My research uncovered a beguiling tale.

In 1914, at the outbreak of war, a fourteen-year-old boy by the name of Thomas Hunt was commencing his studies at St Paul's School. His great-grandfather had been physician to King George IV and author of *The Gold-Headed Cane*. From St Paul's, the young Thomas Hunt won a place at Oxford to study medicine, electing to spend his clinical years at St Mary's Hospital in Paddington: this was to be the start of a lifelong association with the hospital.

Hunt enjoyed a distinguished undergraduate career. He was reputed to have had the best brain at Oxford, at least amongst his fellow undergraduates; and he gained a blue at Oxford for wicket-keeping. At St Mary's he won the coveted Radcliffe prize and two scholarships. On qualifying as a doctor in 1926, Hunt travelled to Berlin and Vienna to study the metabolism of endocrine diseases. On his return to Britain he was appointed to the medical staff of his alma mater – St Mary's. Hunt was much liked by his colleagues, amongst whom his clinical acumen was always held in high esteem.

During the Second World War he served in the Royal Army Medical Corps in West and North Africa and Iraq, and attained the rank of brigadier. On demobilisation, Hunt returned to St Mary's, where he became the hospital's senior physician. He was by all accounts a remarkable man who made outstanding contributions to medicine, clinical practice, university life and his own specialty – gastroenterology.

Hunt was an eloquent and gifted teacher who inspired generations of trainee doctors; his aim was to help students disentangle the immense intricacies of a particular medical conundrum by employing commonsense and plentiful humour. This earned him the uncommon combination of respect and friendship from juniors and students alike.

Doctors who trained at St Mary's in the 1950s say that Dr Hunt would recite *Heredity, sex and age* in the outpatient department, on the wards, indeed anywhere where he saw that a trainee doctor was struggling to fathom disease causation.

Among the medical students at St Mary's Hospital at this time was Eric Finch. Ambitious, driven, and with a quick brain, Finch never struggled. He was destined to succeed not as a physician but as a highly skilled surgeon.

Little over half a century ago, Hunt imparted the single-verse ditty to Finch, who, some forty years later, taught it to me. I had first heard it, as had the rest of my firm, on that autumn day in 1988 when Finch took us to see his man with lung cancer. He had berated the man for *smo*-king and bawled at us, his firm, for our ignorance; he was a gifted teacher and an accomplished surgeon but, blimey, were we afraid of him!

Clinical practice, however, has made me wise so that now I see that underneath Finch's steely veneer was a humane and kind man with an indubitable concern for the welfare of his patients. He cared enormously for his juniors and students, and to this day delights in hearing news of their career successes.

In order for there to be an end, there has to be a beginning. And the beginning of the beginning relates to *aetiology*. Hunt's aide-memoire will be forever entrenched in the minds of medical men and women throughout the world. All will have called upon it in their younger days to deliver themselves from incertitude on some or other ailment, whether in written or viva voce examination, bedside interrogation or routine clinical practice.

The words will always haunt for they act as a simple catalyst to the powerful emotion of memory: that of medical school life, hospital ward rounds, aetiology.